PRR

WHO LIES SLEEPING?

WHO LIES SLEEPING?

*The Dinosaur Heritage
and the Extinction of Man*

MIKE MAGEE

AskWhy! Publications
Selwyn, Frome

First published in Great Britain 1993
by AskWhy! Publications
Selwyn, 41 The Butts, Frome
Somerset, BA11 4AB

Copyright Mike Magee 1988, 1993

ISBN   0-9521913-0-X

Typeset by PCS, Frome
Printed in Great Britain by
Hillman Printers (Frome) Ltd, Somerset

For my parents, Frank and Clarice Magee

"The environmentalists must present their arguments in a sensational form."

Michael Allaby

CONTENTS

Why are we constantly interested in monsters like dinosaurs?
Are the squamous anthropoids that preceded us lying sleeping,
awaiting their opportunity to retrieve the world they lost? A
subliminal awareness of this might explain our obsession with
monsters.

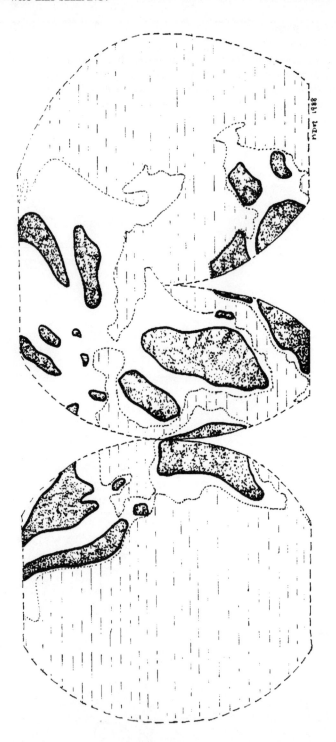

Land
Shallow Sea (Continental Shelf)
Deep Ocean

Approximate position of continents, seas and oceans 85 million years ago

CHAPTER ONE
INTRODUCTION

"One minute gives invention to destroy;
What to rebuild, will a whole age employ."

W.Congreve

Davy Jones' Locker is the legendary repository of everything lost at sea – full of priceless treasures amidst the wrecks of laden merchantmen, cluttered with the jetsam of men desperate to gain a minute's respite on a doomed vessel, strewn with the broken flagships of defeated fleets, and haunted by the bones of sailors crushed in the embrace of the covetous sea. To be in Davy Jones' Locker is not only to be lost geographically, it is to be forgotten too. The sinking of the Titanic was sensational, yet no one knew the huge vessel's resting place until seventy years later when salvagers finally located the wreck.

Five hundred years before, the Mary Rose, pride of the British fleet, unfurled her sails off Spithead only to capsize in shallow water within sight of multitudes on shore cheering the ship on its way to the wars with France. Bulging with sailors and marines the ship, turning too quickly, keeled over and sank, its gun ports, open for the occasion, admitting the callous sea. Though thousands witnessed the tragedy, the site was lost until underwater archaeologists rediscovered it only a few years ago.

This is not a book about accidents at sea. These maritime incidents serve simply to draw a parallel between the ocean and time. Both are guardians of countless secrets. If Davy Jones' Locker beneath the seas is full of forgotten treasure then time's locker must be a trove beyond our conception. For 500 years a shallow estuary concealed the Mary Rose, a wonder of its day. What greater secrets are hidden in time's vast domain?

Let us take three successively longer jumps back in time to see what scholars can reveal of the dark recesses of the past.

The Hittites were a powerful nation, a superpower of their day, sharing the domination of the known world with the Egyptians and the Mesopotamians only 3000 years ago. Yet they disappeared almost without trace. Only the Bible, in references thought to be mythical, preserved their name until modern archaeologists uncovered and identified their ruined cities.

Mankind has been evolving from a common ancestor with the modern apes for several million years, yet scholars know few details of this evolution. Time's coffer still holds secure the history of early man and his precursors. Our knowledge stems from a scant collection of pieces of bone and fragments of skulls, together with chippings and artifacts that a layman cannot distinguish from natural pebbles and flints. We have scarcely revealed any of our prehistory though we are a geologically recent animal.

Vast families of huge creatures lived on this earth for hundreds of millions of years until they died out about 65 million years ago, but they remained unknown to mankind until the end of the 18th century when Baron Cuvier and others began to expose some of time's secrets. They prised time's locker open, only by a chink, but enough for us to know that dinosaurs existed. But the recesses of time's dark chest hides much more about those astonishing beasts than mankind has imagined.

What could we know of an intelligent race of beings that briefly inhabited the world 65 million years ago? Time has not revealed much of them – not sufficient, at any rate, to be recognized by our experts. Yet I shall argue that such a race did inhabit the earth, that it evolved to a similar level of technology to our own and that, as we threaten to do, it destroyed itself in an orgy of selfish and thoughtless excesses that carried into oblivion the last of its own and many other species of the day, including every other remaining dinosaur.

Anthropologists used to think that mankind made discoveries once and then they spread to other peoples and places. Now we know otherwise. Discoveries were made more than once and the centers of ancient civilization were not always the centers of diffusion of skills. Cities in Asia Minor (modern Turkey) are now known to be older than those in the "cradle of civilization" in Mesopotamia; mining of coal and ores for smelting occurred in widely separated prehistoric industrial sites often in areas thought to have been primitive by comparison with the known centers of learning; stone temples built on the Island of Malta predated the pyramids of the mighty Pharaohs; people did not first successfully cultivate wheat in the Fertile Crescent of the Middle East – people on the banks of the river Rhine considered barbarians had succeeded before the Egyptians and Mesopotamians. Agriculture was invented more than once.

If discoveries have been made by different people in different places at different times, could they have been made earlier still, in previous geological epochs, perhaps? We must concede that they could have – perhaps must have! – provided that sufficiently intelligent creatures existed to make the discoveries. But could technological intelligence have arisen in an earlier geological epoch? In the age of the dinosaurs, for example? There's the rub.

Stephen Jay Gould, a noted celebrity in the field of evolution, says most paleontologists regard the development of human-like life anywhere else, even where conditions are similar, as "deterministic". In other words, just because it happened in our case does not mean it will happen for others. They maintain the development of consciousness and intelligence is a "quirky evolutionary accident, a product of one particular lineage". Gould concludes: "Conscious intelligence has emerged only once on earth and presents no real prospects for re-emergence should we choose to use our gift of destruction."

This argument makes mankind unique. It puts us where medieval churchmen placed us – in the center of the universe – and where post-Darwinian Victorians considered us to be – at the apex of evolution. The paleontologists' anthropocentric preconceptions preclude them from asking questions such as "Could the mass extinction of the dinosaurs be self-inflicted?" or "Has intelligence arisen before mankind?" Sir Peter Medawar has noted that "scientists tend not to ask themselves questions until they can see the rudiments of an answer in their minds". In this case the rudiments even of the question did not arise. Men believed mankind to be the pinnacle of creation, indeed created in God's own image. No other animal could have that divine image, no other animal could occupy that unique position, since otherwise man would simply be another beast, another of God's experiments in creation. These questions have not been asked because the answer might be the wrong one. To avoid wrong answers you do not ask questions like these!

Looking beyond mankind's ego, there was another obstacle to the idea of intelligence in dinosaurs. Dinosaurs were believed to be cold-blooded – they were reptiles. Warm-blood seems necessary for a high capacity brain – reptiles and lizards are cold-blooded. Today there is no such objection to the evolution of intelligence in the dinosaurs – they were warm-blooded! They were not cold-blooded and sluggish reptiles – they were not reptiles. And they were active.

Given warm-blooded animals, intelligence could have evolved repeatedly – a conclusion directly contradicting Gould's. On passing a certain threshold intelligence would evolve increasingly rapidly. If the dinosaurs reached the threshold, they could have become intelligent in a geologically short time. Using human evolution as our only example, we can estimate the timescale using the molecular clock.

The molecular clock depends upon natural selection being neutral towards most genes. A beneficial gene survives in a population, but so does a gene that has no particular affect for good or ill. Only genes which confer manifestly disadvantageous characteristics die out through natural selection. Genes continually mutate at a fairly constant rate and, providing that the mutant genes are not harmful, they will spread among a population in which interbreeding freely occurs. Each species therefore has a common gene pool. Once species have separated, their genes no longer mix, there is no longer a common gene pool. If a mutant gene now arises in an animal of one species, it will spread among that species but it cannot spread into the other. The longer the time since two species separated, the greater the difference in genetic and protein structure. Comparing genetic and protein differences between species, and knowing the rate at which the differences multiply, allows us to calculate when speciation occurred.

In 1967, using a molecular dating technique, Victor Sarich and Allan Wilson showed that man diverged from the African apes as little as five million years ago. For orthodox paleontologists this was far too short a time. It spoilt their theories and put us too close for the good of their egos to the apes. They abused Sarich and Wilson and ignored their results for years. Gribbon and Cherfas say it was "as if theoretical astronomers had ignored the discovery of pulsars".

Yet only a few million years ago – perhaps seven million from more recent work – our ancestors were the creatures from which also descended present day chimpanzees. From that time a line branched off the common stock that became human. Mankind apparently reached the threshold of intelligence within perhaps the last five million years. Sixty of the sixty five million years of domination of the earth by mammals elapsed before the intelligent model went into the prototype stage, but then in only about five million years technological society evolved.

Sixty million years of mammalian evolution to arrive at the threshold of intelligence, yet the dinosaurs had 140 million years at the top – twice as long as the mammals. Could animals that succeeded so well for so long fail to develop an intelligent version of their own? There must be a possibility that dinosaurs too achieved thinking status... but 65 million years before us.

If intelligent dinosaurs existed, they must have made a big impression on their world, just as we have. Where then are their ruins, their relics and their kitchen middens?

Consider the following questions. Out of about 12 billion human people that have ever lived on the earth, how many have left any mark? What remains of their accumulated experience? Out of an estimated 80 million species of living organisms on the earth today how many will be classified before they become extinct? How many will leave any fossil remains? How many of the millions of insect species? How many of the estimated 8600 birds? How many of the 4000 mammals? Hardly any! Most living things, intelligent or otherwise do not leave a trace. Species that are constructed mainly of soft tissues which decay quickly effectively leave no fossils. Species that live in environments unconducive to fossilization leave few fossils. Species that evolve and die off quickly leave few remains. Technological civilization only began two hundred years ago and might end in the next hundred. Human civilization, hugely impressive to us, is only an oily smear in the geological record.

In the millions of years that the dinosaurs dominated the earth, thousands of dinosaur species, billions of individuals, have left no trace. If just one of those species came to prominence very rapidly in evolutionary terms, as mankind has, perhaps making no significant mark until its last few centuries, would much be seen in the rocks 65 million years later? I think not, even if anyone were looking for signs of intelligence. And who's looking? Not the paleontologists!

These views are speculative. Experts disdain speculation – though one of Britain's leading thinkers, Richard Dawkins, allows that careful selective speculation can be constructive. Speculative hypotheses face a contradiction: they need more proof than less controversial ones, yet often the absence of convincing evidence is the reason why speculation is necessary. That is true here: direct evidence is sparse and badly documented. Indirect or circumstantial evidence is more plentiful, is generally sound, and constitutes the greater part of this book. Mostly it is culled from popular but authoritative works of science, many written in the last decade, like Bakker's book, "The Dinosaur Heresies". Sources are given in the bibliography for the reader wishing to pursue the detail. Anecdotal evidence fills gaps where studies have been inadequate. Experts, though they defend their own dogmas as determinedly as any medieval prelate, are liable to regard unorthodox ideas with contempt and show little eagerness to investigate them. These experts are often wrong. Though they are technically good at determining facts, they are prone to ignore troublesome ones, and continue to market outmoded theories until well beyond their sell-by date. Worse still, some are inclined to assert whatever is most acceptable to their peers or their paymasters. It pays to be skeptical about such people and wary of their assertions.

Independent writers and researchers in the last couple of decades have put together sufficient to challenge the paleontological dogmatists. Unorthodox proposals deserve attention if only to provoke the experts to justify their conventional arguments and thus periodically to force them into an honest reappraisal. My speculations might stimulate a more open-minded look at past events. Anomalies in old rock strata might be taken seriously and accurately dated rather than ignored. Curious artifacts and impressions in very ancient rocks, of the Cretaceous Period particularly, might be studied systematically to see whether an adequate theory can be constructed to explain them.

More importantly we should examine the parallels between the present time and mass extinctions of the Cretaceous. Tens of millions of years hence, geologists will simply see a sudden reduction in diversity terminating the Tertiary epoch. Will they notice that a couple of inches of sediment contain traces of one species of ape which briefly exploded in numbers prior to the mass extinction? It is doubtful. Is the mass extinction of species the only legacy we wish to leave, as our sapient dinosaurian antecedents did? If my probe into time's vaults motivates enough people to disown our dinosaur heritage and to stop our assault on the planet, we might yet, unlike the dinosaurs, survive.

I am not optimistic!

CHAPTER TWO

EXPERTS AND ICONOCLASTS

"The world would perish were all men learned"

Thomas Fuller

Experts are comedians of error. They claim an authority bounding on infallibility. Yet, from the Eighteenth century to the present day, professors of fossilized remains were wrong and again wrong, not only where evidence was thin on the ground but also often where there was plenty of it. In contrast, many of the great founders of evolutionary theory were amateurs, self taught or untrained in biological sciences: Darwin graduated in divinity; Alfred Russel Wallace, co-discoverer with Darwin of the Theory of Evolution, never graduated – he was trained as a surveyor; Mendel, who worked out the laws of genetics, was a monk. Amateurs are not tied to the conventions of the professional man. They can be more creative, make imaginative leaps with no worries about reputation – they can think the unthinkable. They can speculate.

Today some experts deliberately reject their professional field to become amateurs in another subject where they can speculate to their hearts content. Fred Hoyle is a well known expert in physics, particularly astrophysics. But Hoyle determined to establish himself as an amateur in the new field, for him, of evolutionary theory. He cast off the mantle of the expert to take on a new and speculative role. And it worked, much to the chagrin of some complacent evolutionists, who have had to take time out to answer Hoyle's conjectures. Hoyle might often be wrong in his new role, perhaps he always is, but he is right to force the orthodox to justify themselves rather than propagating dogmas they have never thought to examine.

Experts are human and subject to the failings of us all. In fiction scientists are depicted as inhuman fanatics, as dispassionate robots or abstract old dodderers. Rarely are working scientists any of these in real life. Scientists can be passionate about their pet theories despite their training to be objective, but rarely are they fanatical. Great discoveries have been made through scientists engaging in contests over their competing ideas – gladiators of the Bunsen burner! – the fight ends when successful prediction and application establishes one theory over another. But every established theory will eventually be challenged in its turn as new observations are made.

This is healthy. What is not healthy is when experts set up a scientific establishment with its own rules of acceptance, a scientific freemasonry from which others are excluded. Theories no longer belong to individuals but to the group, whose vested interest is served by cleaving to them and ridiculing alternatives. New thought is stifled while yesterday's innovation, a dynamic force for progress, becomes a new orthodoxy, and establishment opinion becomes oppressively conservative. Members of the fraternity and those aspiring to it may even become liars and forgers if status and respect is gained or retained thereby. They falsify results and even create imaginary co-workers in their desperation for approval and recognition. Still worse is when scientists sell their objectivity for pieces of silver – when they are employed by governments and businesses to defend their employers' position and take a partisan view irrespective of the facts. For the general public these are the really dangerous experts.

Thomas Kuhn explains the stability and overthrow of established scientific theories in his book, "The Structure of Scientific Revolutions". Science is conducted within an accepted framework of thought which he calls a "paradigm". Everyone is happy with it until at some stage it is challenged – someone has a better idea. Learned professors choke into their port at High Table thinking, "All our work is out of date – our research programs are irrelevant." But their defences are ready. They close ranks, rally to the orthodox view and hasten to discredit the innovators.

The leading modern paleontological iconoclast, Robert Bakker, found himself up against the establishment when he urged vigorously that the physiology and lifestyles of dinosaurs should be reassessed. He later expressed it thus: "Old theories are tough antagonists in court. The scientific establishment tends to believe that old, accepted views are correct unless shown to be wrong beyond any reasonable doubt". Exactly! Equally good theories find it difficult to get a fair hearing in the experts' court where the scientific establishment supply counsel for the prosecution, officials, judge and jury, all of whom back the conventional view.

Not long ago Rupert Sheldrake's theory of morphogenetic fields (which suggests that once something has happened it is more likely to happen again) was violently attacked by many of his scientific peers. The editor of a respected scientific journal virtually recommended that his book should be burned. Sheldrake's theory might prove to be worthless – but only by testing it can we find out. However the allocation of research funds depends upon peer group recommendation and, needless to say, those wishing to test this controversial hypothesis could not get financial support.

Those who defend the old paradigm are the majority of established scientists in the field, at least at the beginning. The revolutionaries, the new thinkers, attack it. Competition takes place and the paradigm holds or it falls. If the latter, the new paradigm becomes accepted and is destined to become the canon in its turn. As T.H.Huxley put it: new truths begin as heresies and end as superstitions.

What then is the lesson of this? Simply to remain open minded. And that does not mean to remain sitting on the fence. Since science progresses through the jousting of different ideas until one is unseated, there is nothing wrong with people defending their theory during the tournament. What is wrong is closing one's mind to the merits of other ideas and, what is worse, closing ranks against them. It is openness, receptiveness, the desire to look at something new, that helps to keep societies and their methodologies healthy. Dogma of any kind puts a straitjacket on the mind and a jackboot on society.

Of course, some proposals will have little merit and will fall quickly when assailed by the evidence – but something is usually gained in the exercise. Bakker, writing about the publication of novel ideas in science, says that even when the revolutionary idea finally proves not correct, the natural tendency to accept orthodoxy unchallenged is beneficially shaken.

Let me give you examples of some comedians of error, some defenders of orthodoxy and some heroes of invention involved in the fields of enquiry most relevant to the subject of this book, paleontology and prehistory.

Baron Cuvier realized before Queen Victoria came to the throne of England that extinction is the fate of us all. Cuvier was born in 1769 and lived his younger life before the French revolution when opportunities for young talented people not of the aristocratic class were limited. As a consequence, after completing his studies, he had to take a lowly post as a tutor in Normandy. But the French Revolution created new opportunities and Cuvier took charge of the Jardin des Plantes in Paris. Continuing his studies there he successively became a professor of natural history and then of anatomy. The famous mosasaurus found in 1770, which created the original scientific interest in fossils, was identified by Cuvier as an extinct marine lizard.

The spirit of the time imbued Cuvier. He was keen that the French masses should appreciate the wonders of science and nature; but he was not willing simply to wait for people deprived for centuries of mental stimuli to recognize he had something of value. He wanted to create a market for learning, to attract his audience by presenting natural history in novel and exciting ways. His solution was to practise the techniques of showmen and actors. Teaching himself to be a dramatic and persuasive lecturer, choosing analogies he knew laborers and peasants could understand, he won the working people to the thrill of discovery. He even opened his own library for their use.

He also sought – and received – assistance for his endeavors from government, persuading Napoleon that he should provide museums with well conceived, visually interesting displays and should donate money for research. His imaginative ideas succeeded and Cuvier not only became a national hero, receiving his title as an honor, he also became internationally renowned.

Cuvier was one of the founders of the study of historical geology or stratigraphy. The other was an Englishman, William Smith. Cuvier had noticed how different rock strata had different fossils in them. The topmost layers of recent deposits contained familiar bones but the deeper down he looked the less familiar they were. William Smith was a surveyor and could not fail to notice fossils in the rocks in the everyday execution of his duties. From his observations he proposed that rocks could be dated by the fossils in them, their index fossils. He catalogued them, thereby providing the first reliable geological clock which could be used for dating widely separated rocks. Cuvier and Smith had erected the two pillars of stratigraphy: (1) normally younger rocks lie on top of older ones; (2) rocks containing the same fossils are the same age.

From these beginnings the scientific study of the earth and prehistory could begin in earnest. Scholars began to look with fresh interest at the rocks, to the natural formations around them, stimulated by the works of the pioneers. They were astonished by the huge petrified bones that were common in some strata.

The Biblical deluge of Noah's Ark was the orthodox explanation of the fossilized remains of extinct animals, but Cuvier realized it could not explain all the changes from stratum to stratum. He decided there must have been a series of such catastrophes. After each extinction God began again. The theory of catastrophes was published as "A Discourse on the Revolutions of the Surface of the Globe". Cuvier perceptively noted: "whole races were extinguished leaving mere traces of their existence, which are now difficult of recognition, even by a naturalist".

Exhibit 1. Baron Cuvier

The study of fossilized bones under the rocks and their identification as extinct species were, because of prevailing religious views, controversial from the start. The Bible was regarded by many, even learned people, as being the infallible word of God and unquestionably true. Though Cuvier was much admired as a scholar his book was regarded by many in the British establishment, the ecclesiastical and political experts of the day, as dangerously radical. It contradicted the Bible! Cuvier's scientifically observed catastrophe theory had to do battle with the dogma of Noah's Flood.

Furthermore, according to the Church's teaching of "plenum", God had created the world complete – nothing could have been taken away or added. Dinosaur bones had been emerging from eroding rocks for longer than man had existed, testifying to the extinction of species and the evolution of new ones. Yet the Church dogma of "plenum" forbade such a heresy. Religious bigotry resulted in English publishers bowdlerizing Cuvier's book to give the impression that Cuvier was approving Noah's deluge not proposing a radically new and more general theory challenging Church dogmata.

Moreover God's world was thoroughly anthropocentric. Mankind's rightful place was at the center of creation. Darwin was soon to have trouble over this and respectable paleontologists still believe it today. But a catastrophe theory must admit of the likelihood of future catastrophes eventually even sweeping away mankind – a thought inconceivable to the ecclesiastical experts.

How were species replaced after each catastrophe? Cuvier did not go so far as to advocate evolution. His idea was one of separate creations after each destruction. Evolutionary theory had to wait for Charles Darwin. But fear of confrontation with the clerics obliged Darwin to hold up publication while he sought to amass enough evidence to put the issue beyond doubt. He also spent time seeking noncontroversial examples. Only at the end of "On the Origin of Species" did he reveal the direction of his thoughts: "light will be thrown on the origin of man and his history".

The pressure on innovative thinkers in this stifling atmosphere of intolerance is well illustrated by Cuvier's predecessor, Le Comte de Buffon, who initially believed correctly that mastodon remains found in the 18th century on the banks of the Ohio river were a new species of animal, but later was shamed into retracting and admitting that they were after all only a mixture of elephant tusks and hippopotamus teeth.

Buffon did have the courage to argue that the geological history of the earth was longer than the Biblical scholars reckoned. He calculated that a molten globe the size of the earth would have taken at least 75,000 and perhaps 500,000 years to cool. His longer estimate was ten thousand times too short but ten thousand per cent better than the theologians' preference – Bishop Ussher's now risible estimate (calculated from Biblical lineages) that the earth was created in 4004 BC!

Cuvier's fossil specimens were often fragmentary – they usually still are – but he was not fazed. From comparative anatomy he concluded that the different parts of an animal were so closely connected that the whole creature could be reconstructed from a single bone. Cuvier had become an expert! Much *can* be learned about an animal from only a few remains, but Cuvier's excessive confidence, which inspired later paleontologists, was misplaced and led to serious mistakes. Excessive confidence is a key characteristic of experts.

G.A.Mantell, a professional physician, was an amateur paleontologist whose pleasure was to hunt for fossils and who, perhaps because of his obsession with his hobby, lost his money, his wife and his family, and died in relative obscurity. In his happier days however his fossil hunting brought him recognition. He was the first man to identify a tooth of an iguanodon, a herbivorous dinosaur. (Cuvier thought it was a hippopotamus tooth.) Yet a rival almost deprived him of his precedence. An authority on fossils at that time, the Reverend Buckland, advised Mantell not to publish until he was certain of his identification. Buckland, who had also found dinosaur fossils, had no intention of hanging about. He quickly prepared a description of his own discovery, megalosaurus, a large carnivorous dinosaur from the Jurassic, and published it a year before Mantell published his on iguanodon. Scholars now base Mantell's prior claim on his earlier lectures and his notebooks which showed the thoroughness of his work and the originality of his thinking.

Buckland's motives might have been sincere. Perhaps he did not wish to see the enthusiastic Mantell disillusioned by the possibility of ridicule. Be that as it may, Buckland's own prejudices exposed him to ridicule on a different occasion. He identified the ten thousand year old skeleton of a young cave man as a Romano-British camp follower. The bones were found among remains of animals now extinct in a cave in South Wales. Buckland, a Biblical as well as a geological expert, assumed these animals had perished in the Flood but, since the descendants of Adam had not lived in Britain before the Flood, the human remains had to be later. Nearby were the ruins of a Roman camp. The Reverend noted that the dead person wore beads and, since men do not wear beads, the skeleton, despite the anatomical evidence, had to be that of a woman. Buckland concluded, "whatever may have been her occupation, the vicinity of a camp would afford... a means of subsistence". Ever since, Buckland's mistaken identification has been derided as "The Red Lady of Paviland", a double entendre, the bones being red with iron oxide.

Buckland even failed to draw appropriate conclusions from his own specimen, the megalosaurus, which had teeth set in sockets like crocodiles' not growing straight out of the jawbones like lizards'. Though Buckland explained why the anatomical features of the fossil proved it was not a crocodile, his mental fixation, his unquestioning acceptance of the conceptual paradigms of the period, stopped him from appreciating the enormous significance of his findings: he had almost discovered the dinosaurs.

When progress is imprisoned by the experts' paradigms (or preconceptions, call them what you will) the break out is frequently the work of the astute amateur. An appropriate example is the discovery of the nature of the ichthyosaur. It also illustrates how accident rather than design so often in science reveals what was previously hidden.

The fossils found with the remains of the ichthyosaur showed that it was a marine animal. They lived in schools because wherever there were deposits "they were as tightly packed in that slate as herrings in a barrel". William Daniel Conybeare, an Englishman who wrote the first monograph on the ichthyosaur, drew it as a lizard with paddle-like limbs, while Cuvier described it as "a creature with the snout of a dolphin, the teeth of a crocodile, the skull and the chest of a lizard, the paddles of a whale, and the vertebrae of a fish". This is not an unreasonable description, but how were these components put together, what was its actual shape and what was its lifestyle?

The experts reasoned thus: being reptiles, they must have laid eggs; marine turtles have to shuffle their way up beaches to do this, the ichthyosaurs must have done the same; they would not have looked very elegant but then turtles do not either, though they manage; walruses and seals are also clumsy on land yet they also manage; ergo, ichthyosaurs were ill-adapted amphibious lizards.

Enter the famous Victorian paleontologist, Richard Owen, a very remarkable man of considerable genius who suffered only from becoming an expert. Having trained with Cuvier in Paris, coined the word dinosaur in 1841, and established himself as an authority on comparative anatomy, Owen, despite his successes, was able to demonstrate, with immense confidence, how spectacularly wrong he could be. A confirmed anthropocentrist and anti-evolutionist, he classified mankind as being unique in all creation and sought to prove it by listing human anatomical features that were similarly unique. T.H.Huxley toppled humans and Owen from their respective pedestals by showing that all of the "unique" features chosen by Owen were present in the great apes!

From his examination of the ichthyosaur fossil Owen successfully showed that the creature had tendons attaching muscles from its tail to its bones indicating that, like whales, the ichthyosaurs used their tails to power themselves through the water. The difference was that the ichthyosaur's tail fin was vertical whereas the whale's tail fin was horizontal. An odd thing was that all specimens seemed to have broken tails; about a third of the way along, the tail vertebrae bent downwards. Owen felt that the tail must have broken after death but before fossilization. As the corpse of the dead animal drifted around gradually decaying, at some stage the tail had dropped under its own weight but tendons kept it attached to the body so that it became fossilized apparently broken.

This was the picture of the ichthyosaur until the 1890s when Bernard Hauff, the owner of a few slate quarries at Holzmaden near Stuttgart in Germany, raised himself to a remarkable level of proficiency in cleaning fossil-bearing slate slabs.

In 1892 someone carelessly spilled a glass of water on to a slab that Hauff was cleaning. No one thought anything of the accident itself, the water would dry leaving the specimen perfectly all right. But amazingly Hauff saw that, as the water dried, it revealed the living outline of the ichthyosaur.

Though skilled at cleaning slates, Hauff was still an amateur as far as the interpretation of any of the fossil specimens was concerned. A few days later, therefore, when some experts led by Professor Oscar Fraas from the Stuttgart Natural History Museum called by, he asked them whether it was possible for the soft tissues of an animal to fossilize. If so he would spend time trying to bring out the outline as clearly as possible. "Absolutely no possibility of it at all, my dear Hauff, Don't bother to waste your time over it. Just carry on with the excellent work you are already doing. The stains must be simply some peculiar property of the slate," was their dismissive reaction.

Fortunately Herr Hauff was not put off by these learned opinions and the next time the museum's experts visited he was able to show them the impression of an ichthyosaur's skeleton within its skin, the tail fin and dorsal fin clearly showing.

Hauff's lucky accident, his unwillingness to obey the voice of authority and his astonishing skill answered many questions and offered the authorities an altogether more streamlined, fish-like creature than they had imagined. The ichthyosaur was fully adapted for its marine existence. The bend in its tail bones was natural and not caused by breakage. It supported the lower part of a crescent shaped tail fin, rather like a shark's except that in the shark the cartilaginous support extends into the upper part of the fin. The dorsal fin was totally unexpected. The ichthyosaur was a saurian dolphin not a brother to the turtle or even a saurian sea lion. On land it would have been just as helpless as a whale. But if ichthyosaurs could not move about on land how did they lay their eggs? More of that later.

Bernard Hauff was not obedient to authority; he did not accept the dogmas of the experts. He went on to show that all good ichthyosaur specimens from Holzmaden had a skin. He was eventually rewarded with an honorary doctorate.

In fairness to Oscar Fraas, he was delighted by the discoveries, although he did briefly argue that the dorsal fin was just one of a series of lizard like vanes running down the ichthyosaur's back. That view was soon demolished by further specimens given the Hauff treatment.

Evidently experts either see more than is there or nothing at all. They are either omniscient or nescient, seeing all or seeing nothing depending upon whether new observations slot into their paradigm or not. Those expecting only the conventional can be, to all intents and purposes, truly blind. John Ostrom of Yale University relates the story of how he found the clawed hand of a dinosaur, subsequently called deinonychus, protruding from an eroded mound. Yet only feet away were the recent footprints of his team of experts who, while prospecting the site for specimens, had passed by missing it completely.

On the other hand Richard Owen's training with Cuvier seemed to give him a degree of omniscience. Given a mere fragment of fossilized bone, he was able to identify it as "a struthious bird nearly equal in size to the ostrich, belonging to a heavier and more sluggish species." In this instance Owen was spot on: the bone proved to be one of the giant moas of New Zealand, quite unknown at the time.

That shows expertise at its best. What of its worst? Paleontologists had a bias for the aquatic lifestyle of the duck-billed hadrosaurs. The well known dinosaur classifier, Joseph Leidy, had originally thought them aquatic because they had beaks rather like a duck's and an animal with a bill must feed like a duck and ergo be aquatic like a duck. The logic is impeccable, don't trouble us with facts! Direct evidence testified otherwise. The petrified contents of the hadrosaur's stomach included twigs, needles from conifers and the remains of willow and poplar, showing that the creature browsed on lowland forest trees not on soft weed in slow moving rivers or lakes.

To construct and name new species from inadequate fragments is fraught with hazards even if you are an Owen or a Cuvier. For lesser men it is mayhem. Witness the variety of species described initially as being megalosaurus. After William Buckland's description in 1824, any partial remains of Jurassic carnivores were attributed to megalosaurus. Reports of it came in from all over Europe and as far afield as Australia and North America. David Norman, an authority on dinosaurs, says that at least 26 instances have occurred. Trying to sort them out causes more muddle. Omniscience replaces nescience and suddenly the classifiers have not one but lots of different species.

Neither the original specimen nor the others were sufficient to merit the attempts to name them. A complication of tyrannosaurid teeth is that their shape varies from the front to the back of the jaw. Experts attempting "a Cuvier" or "an Owen" came to think that differently shaped teeth came from different animals. The result was a variety of names given by different authorities at different times to bits of the same animal.

Norman comments: "This welter of names provides yet another example of how dangerous it can be to name new species on the basis of inadequate material... If these scientists had resisted the temptation to name the teeth until better material, such as skull and jaws had been discovered, much confusion could have been avoided."

To judge how the intelligent dinosaur might have evolved, we shall be looking at the evolution of mankind, the intelligent mammal. Here again experts were at work debunking new ideas and discoveries just as they had in other realms. The discovery of fragments of a skull and skeleton of a primitive man at Neanderthal in the mid-Nineteenth century aroused widespread interest but impressed the experts little.

"It is not a primitive skull at all,"they announced. "It is merely the skull of a Dutchman," offered one German anatomist (German anatomists at that time being highly respected). Another expert retorts, "Nonsense, it is the skull of a Cossack who died while pursuing Napoleon's retreating armies in 1812". Thomas Huxley dryly observed that this Cossack had removed his clothes in a freezing continental January, disposed of them, climbed a 60 feet high cliff, died, and buried himself. "It plainly is thick skulled so it must be an Irishman," reasoned yet another expert, this time French. "You are all quite wrong," announced Rudolf Virchow, the doyen of German pathologists. "The poor man's unusual features are nothing to do with primitiveness but are simply due to rickets and arthritis together with some severe buffeting about the head."

These learned men failed to appreciate the antiquity of the skull which was thereafter put away and forgotten for many years. Then Marcellin Boule of the French Museum of natural history published three tomes, supposedly seminal, on it from 1910 to 1913. Boule was so astonishingly lacking in objectivity that his work defies explanation even for an expert. Let us merely highlight his most well known error which was to fail to take account of the poor man's arthritis, noted correctly by Virchow, which was cripplingly severe and had seriously distorted his body. The skeleton was that of an old man.

His conclusions influenced subsequent generations into thinking that Neanderthal man was brutish, dim-witted and subhuman. Today "Neanderthal" is still a term of abuse even though W.Strauss and A.J.Cave wrote this about Neanderthal man in the 1950s: "If he could be reincarnated and placed in a New York subway, provided he were bathed, shaved and dressed in modern clothing, it is doubtful whether he would attract any more attention than some of its other denizens". Indeed one wonders whether a Neanderthal man would risk travelling alone on the New York subway.

Over a hundred years ago Edouard Piette discovered that Homo sapiens had domesticated horses in very early times. The most respected authority of the time, the Abbe Breuil, another churchman, vigorously rejected the idea. Piette died at the turn of the century and it was not until 1966 that the question was reopened with the description of a 15,000 years old carving of a horse's head in a quite elaborate bridle. If horses were being handled in this sophisticated way 15,000 years ago there is strong reason to believe that horses were captured and held tethered in less sophisticated ways many thousands of years before that. In fact, there is evidence from the wear of horses' teeth 30,000 years old that they were tethered even then.

Learned men proved their blindness more recently when Raymond Dart, an anatomist at the University of Witwatersrand in South Africa, discovered the skull of the Taung child. Sir Arthur Keith, Keeper of the Hunterian Collection at the Royal College of Surgeons, at first seemed supportive but then dismissed Dart's claim that the skull was hominid. "It is the skull of a young chimpanzee," pronounced Keith. Hominid jaws are distinguished from other apes by the lack of large canine teeth and the corresponding absence of a gap (the diastema) in the opposing set of teeth to accommodate the canines when the jaw is closed. The Taung skull had small, human-like canines and no diastema proving to any anatomical tyro that the skull was not a chimpanzee's. Keith's fellow experts, Sir Arthur Smith-Woodward, Sir Grafton Elliot and Dr W.L.H.Duckworth, all blind as moles, joined in the skepticism in varying degrees towards Dart's discovery. Only as he approached 80 did Keith concede that he had been wrong about the Taung child. For that he deserves some praise – most experts are not gracious enough to admit it though they know they *are* wrong.

Keith was so blind that he confirmed the blatant forgery, the Piltdown skull, as authentic, naming it Eoanthropus Dawsonii, after its discoverer and possible forger. Woodward, who had been present at the Piltdown site, backed him in his judgment. Woodward went on to devote most of the later part of his life to the Piltdown skull, going so far as to write a book about it with the appalling title, "The First Englishman". One wonders whether later Englishmen were as ignominious as the first. Only those who are experts, perhaps.

Blindness struck a footprint expert only to be followed by omniscience. According to Don Johanson, discoverer of Lucy, the most complete hominid skeleton yet found, the astonishing pre-human footprints at Laetoli were almost ignored. American footprint specialist, Louise Robbins pronounced that the first print discovered was merely that of a horse.

Paul Abell (who had found the print under the turf), Tim White and Peter Jones felt sure the print was hominid and wanted to continue excavating, hoping to find prints that were more easily identifiable. Because they were not specialists in footprints, Mary Leakey, for many years one of Britain's topmost paleoanthropologists, who was directing the excavation, felt obliged to respect the opinion of her footprint professional. She ordered that the scarce resources of the team should be used elsewhere. But, faced with the protests of the trio, she then agreed to compromise by putting one of the untrained native workers on to the job. Only after the trainee successfully revealed several more human looking footprints did Mary Leakey relent and agree to put Tim White in charge of excavating the tracks.

They proved to extend for almost 30 yards and induced a miracle – Louise Robbins' skepticism suddenly turned to revelation. She not only conceded that the prints were hominid but found her expertise returning to such an extent that she knew which prints were male and which were female, that the female prints were those of a pregnant ape and that the apes came from a line of bipedal walkers that stretched back for a million years. Johanson does not record whether she revealed the sex of the pregnant lady's baby!

Don Johanson also illustrates the extent to which offended experts aim to go to revenge themselves. Johanson was attending a conference in New York in 1974. He had just announced his remarkable find of the knee joint of an ape over three million years old which showed that its owner was plainly bipedal and therefore seemed to be in the direct human line. At lunch, Mary Leakey told him she had overheard some anatomists saying they were positive the knee was that of a monkey. Carried away with self-assured expert malevolence they agreed to "wait until he goes into print, then we'll carve him up". But Johanson's identification was sound – he was not carved up.

It can be even worse. Dr Harold Hillman, a medical doctor and qualified research worker with degrees in neurobiology and physiology joined an English university as a lecturer and soon became its director of Applied Physiology. His credentials seemed admirable and for ten years he was highly respected in his field – until 1980. In that year Hillman criticized much of the basis of biochemical research. He claimed techniques for preparing tissues for the electron microscope altered the structures of the tissue being examined. The electron microscope has, on the face of it, been a great boon to biologists because it gives beautiful pictures under huge magnification with a depth of field that is veritably three dimensional. It apparently shows immense details of the very basic processes of life.

But Hillman questioned the validity of what was seen when the preparation of the sample was so harsh that the original structures were lost or modified and spurious structures replaced them. Even to a layman the question seems justified when it is considered that the scientists are taking samples of living cells which are largely water, drying them out, coating them with molecules of gold and finally belting them with beams of electrons to create the picture. The electron microscope depends on electrons mimicking light in an optical microscope: they have to travel in straight lines and so have to be in a vacuum otherwise molecules of air knock them in all directions. In a vacuum any water present in the sample would evaporate and likewise scatter the electrons. The gold coating makes sure that the electrons *do* get deflected efficiently where they should be – from the surface of the sample – to ensure a clear photograph.

If the structures seen in an electron microscope are often artifacts of the techniques of preparation of the samples, as Hillman claims to have demonstrated, then a lot of experts are spending a lot of money concocting theories that depend only on what has been created by accident in the laboratory.

Hillman was removed from teaching – even of topics unconnected with his criticisms. He was told that his work was unorthodox and of little general merit, that there were insufficient funds to support it and that he should retire. Hillman protested and found an independent source of funds for a year. But the authorities moved the goalposts – he had to find funding for three to five years. Hillman's views might be thought damaging by those whose electron microscope is a nice little earner of reputations and whose interests are vested in a nice set of comfortable theories generated thereby, but that is not the point. The UK Sloman report, which was published in response to a different case of academic disagreement, said quite forcefully, "academic staff must not be inhibited by any tradition of accepted views. They have the right to be unorthodox."

"Some of the greatest advances in science have come about because some clever person spotted an analogy between a subject that was readily understood, and another still mysterious subject," writes Richard Dawkins. Yet he warns that one of the hallmarks of futile crankiness is overenthusiastic analogizing. The trick is to strike a balance. The successful scientist and the raving crank are separated by the quality of their inspirations. Which amounts to an ability to reject foolish analogies and to pursue helpful ones.

It sounds reasonable. But is it really wise to inhibit originality even if cranky? Who knows how many important ideas do not see the light of day because their originator feels wrongly they are a bit too cranky, or is timid about the response of his peers. What is the criterion of the quality of an inspiration other than the influence it ultimately has? Perhaps scientific journals should have a section entitled, "Wildly Speculative Letters" in which overenthusiastic analogizing is encouraged.

Dawkins does not like what he regards as ill-founded attacks by creationists and others critics of evolutionary theory. Yet out of these attacks has come Dawkins own brilliant book, "The Blind Watchmaker", defending the theory. Perhaps he will concede that good can come even of cranky ideas even if indirectly.

Many will regard the proposals put in this book as cranky. That is why I have devoted space to seeking to persuade the reader that: (1) experts are fallible, yet; (2) they are so cocksure they consider it a philanthropic duty to suppress those who contradict them; (3) unorthodox thinkers have a right to be unorthodox; (4) good can come of crankiness. If you are not so persuaded then you can read on for amusement or put the book down, as you wish. Otherwise you can read on with the confidence that some unorthodox, interesting and perhaps frightening views will be unveiled.

CHAPTER THREE

JUST BIG LIZARDS

"No non-dinosaur larger than a turkey walked the land in the age of the dinosaurs."

Robert Bakker

Many would say it is absurd to imagine intelligence in dinosaurs, cold-blooded, lumbering beasts with brains the size of walnuts. But is it so absurd? Were dinosaurs so primitive? They were considered so for many years but in the 70s, two American professors, John Ostrom and Robert Bakker, drove a coach and four through previously held dogmas about these astonishing beasts. They argued convincingly that dinosaurs were not just big lizards, cold-blooded and sluggish – dinosaurs were hot-blooded. Like mammals and, especially, like birds they had a high metabolic rate and an active lifestyle.

These new ideas provide a base for the reassessment of intelligence in dinosaurs. Hot-bloodedness changes the picture completely. The evidence for it is crucially important to the thesis presented here and justifies some detailed attention in this chapter.

The earliest large fossils that had been found were recognized by the authorities of the time like Baron Cuvier, Dr Mantell and the Reverend Buckland as being those of reptiles, similar to the monitor lizard and the iguana. These modern lizards are all cold-blooded. Strictly their blood is not cold but, unlike birds and mammals, they have no internal thermostat to keep their temperature constant. In cold weather their blood temperature drops and they become sluggish and inactive, but when the sun shines they bask in it until their temperature rises, then they become active and seek some sustenance. If the sun gets too hot they shelter in the shade or try to expose the minimum surface area to the sun's rays to absorb less heat to prevent overheating.

When dinosaur fossils were first recognized, being lizard-like, they were classified as being of cold-blooded animals – though Richard Owen, who first categorized the dinosaurs, realized that, in many respects, they were more advanced than lizards and crocodiles. But it was the picture of a giant lizard that prevailed rather than that of a more advanced creature – until Bakker and Ostrom came along. Owen's definitive paper was written in 1841, yet almost 130 years later Robert Bakker could write that paleontologists still regarded dinosaurs as overgrown lizards in respect of their everyday behavior. Because crocodiles and lizards spent much of their lives in inactivity, sunning themselves on a convenient rock, the brontosaurus was pictured as a rotund, long necked crocodile moving about slowly and infrequently, and basking whenever it could in the sun.

Was this picture of such amazingly successful animals correct? Were they really just big lizards? If they were, their physiology, the physical construction of their bodies, would have meant that they were severely handicapped creatures. Let us take a look at these handicaps.

- Lungs.

Lungs are spongy air sacs with millions of tiny, thin walled lobes containing circulating blood to absorb oxygen from the air. The smaller the tiny air lobes, the greater the surface area exposed to the inhaled air and the more efficient the absorption of oxygen. In a lizard these lobes are not miniscule as they are in mammals, they are larger and correspondingly inefficient.

In the human mammal destruction of the walls between the tiny air cells, by smoking cigarettes, for example, reduces the surface available for the exchange of oxygen causing a chronic and totally debilitating disease, emphysema. People with emphysema suffer from oxygen deficiency and have to move slowly. Pure oxygen inhalers help a little. Lizards effectively have to live their whole lives with emphysema: they are unable to take in much oxygen, their blood does not get much and their activity is correspondingly curtailed.

In contrast, birds, which have some lizard-like features (witness the scales on their legs, for example), have highly efficient lungs to support their active lifestyle. Yet many dinosaurs had hollow bones containing additional air sacs connected to their lungs just like birds. Did they have bird-like lungs with subsidiary air sacs pushing air steadily through in one direction, much more efficient than mammals' lungs in which the air travels first one way then the other. This alone could have ensured the dinosaurs' superiority for millions of years. But did it also make them more prone to gaseous or particulate pollution contributing to their eventual extinction?

- Heart.

A lizard's heart is particularly inefficient because it has only one main pumping chamber or ventricle whereas mammals have two. Two ventricles are more efficient. The oxygenated blood from the lungs can be kept separated from the oxygen depleted blood returning from the body. In humans "blue babies" are born with a hole in their heart, not a hole to the outside of the heart – blood does not escape – a hole between two of the chambers of the heart allowing oxygenated and spent blood to mix. Consequently, the capacity of the blood for oxygen is not fully utilized. The blue baby's arteries always carry some spent blood, which is dark in color unlike oxygenated blood which is bright red, giving it a blue look instead of the normal pink. In a lizard the two bloodstreams have to enter the single ventricle where they mix just as they do in the heart of a blue baby. Lizards are like mammals with a hole in the heart.

A zoologist, Roger Seymour of Adelaide University, researched into the connection between the difference in height between the heart and the brain of sauropod dinosaurs and the blood pressure needed to push the blood up to that height. If the animals were browsing from high branches then high blood pressures would obviously be required (a giraffe's blood pressure is twice that of a man) and to generate such high pressures the heart would have to be sophisticated. It would certainly need four chambers not two like lizards. High browsing dinosaurs, if no others, must have had four-chambered hearts like this and, if they had them, it is probable that the others had too.

- Bone.

Bone is not simply a dead inorganic material which only provides the internal framework of a vertebrate's body, it is also an important living organ equivalent to the heart and the lungs. The bone marrow is where blood cells are made and the bones act as a reserve of calcium, a mineral that is essential in the functioning of muscle.

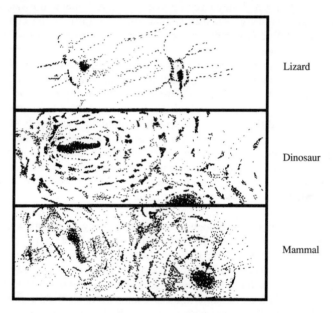

Exhibit 2. Diagram of bone sections showing Haversian systems

Naturally the efficient working of bone in these tasks depends upon a liberal supply of blood to transport the organ's products to the sites in the body where they are needed. Mammals and birds have a complex system of blood supply through the bones but in reptiles the blood supply is much more feeble. Growth is slow in the warm days of summer and stops altogether in the winter giving annual growth rings like those in trees or on tortoise shells. The exchange of calcium between the bones and the blood occurs in structures called the Haversian canals which are relatively lacking in reptile bones.

In 1988 Robin Reid of Belfast University published an extensive survey of bone structure. He found that reptiles could have a mammalian type of bone structure, particularly if they were large or grew in hot temperatures. What of dinosaurs? Sometimes they had reptilian and sometimes mammalian types of bone but most dinosaur bone is of the warm-blooded variety, whereas it is unusual for reptiles to have it.

Reptilian physiology obliges reptiles to be slow and to conserve their energy. Compared with mammals they suffer from almost crippling defects of lungs, heart and bone. Unlike mammals their bodies simply cannot sustain continuous effort. That is why they move jerkily and spend long periods totally motionless.

Adrian Desmond, author of "The Hot-Blooded Dinosaurs", says the monstrous carnivorous dinosaur, tyrannosaurus rex, could have reached no more than three or four mph if it were cold-blooded. You or I would have little need to fear such a creature – if we jogged away from it, it could not catch us moving even at its fastest. Yet it gives every appearance of being built for speed as well as strength. Indeed for almost a hundred years dinosaurs have been illustrated as active creatures. Just after the turn of the century, Charles Beecher of Yale University constructed a mock-up of a hadrosaur, claosaurus, in a running posture.

From analyzing dinosaur tracks we know a dinosaur' normal walking pace was faster than would be expected for the maximum speed of an equal sized lizard. McNeil Alexander of Britains's Leeds University has a formula for working out travelling velocities from imprints of an animal's tracks. Carnivorous dinosaurs seemed to travel commonly at speeds of between five and ten miles per hour. Herbivores sauntered around apparently at about four miles per hour. A fast walking pace for a human being is about three miles an hour so these speeds are respectable for large animals no more likely to be making haste than a grazing cow. And, like the cow, when the occasion demanded it they could move a lot faster.

"Even a cursory glance at dinosaurian limbs and joints," says Adrian Desmond, "should be evidence enough that many dinosaurs were built on the same lines as modern hoofed mammals". A useful yet simple guideline in this respect is the length of the shinbone to the thigh bone. Relatively slow moving animals have longer thighs than shins whereas swift animals have evolved longer bones in their lower leg giving them a longer stride to increase their speed. Take a look at some modern animals: the elephant rarely has need for speed and its shins are shorter than its thighs, the ratio being about 0.6. A gazelle needs speed as its means of avoiding predators – its shins are 1.25 times longer than its thighs, the highest such ratio of all animals.

What do we know from the fossil record of the shin to thigh ratios of dinosaurs? The brontosaurus had short shins compared with its thighs similar to an elephant's – both are heavy, slow moving, browsing animals. What of the hadrosaurs? Their shins were between 0.8 and 0.9 times the length of their thighs, much longer than the brontosaurus's (and the elephant's) but much smaller than the gazelle. It seems that, relatively, they were faster than an elephant but not as fast as a gazelle. So, what modern animal is comparable? The racehorse! A racehorse's shinbone is about 0.9 of the length of its thighbone showing that the hadrosaurs occupied a similar ecological niche. Finding similar leg measurements on modern animals and dinosaur fossils suggests similar lifestyles.

Another sensitive measure is the length of the middle metatarsal (middle toe) to the thighbone, because fast running animals tend to lift themselves on to their toes to increase their stride still further. The brontosaurus had a middle toe to thigh ratio the same as that of an elephant (0.13). Dinosaurs evidently built for speed were the coelurosaurs which had a middle toe 0.77 of the length of its thigh comparing favorably with a horse (0.78).

Sometimes the similarities went further. Indeed dinosaurs could be so astonishingly similar to modern beasts that it is difficult to accept they did not have the same ecological role. The coelurosaurs occupied the biological niche now held by the ostriches and similar flightless birds. Characteristic of them was the struthiomimus, so called because it was felt to mimic the ostrich (Struthio camelus). It is aptly named because its similarity to the ostrich is quite remarkable.

- It was seven feet tall, slightly taller than an ostrich.
- Its back was short and its hind legs were long.
- It had a shin to thigh ratio of 1.0 with its leg length effectively increased by an additional extended metatarsal bone.
- Its mouth was toothless and beak-like.
- It might even have had a flap of skin from its arms to its body to perform the same role as the ostrich's wings when it was running.

There is only one essential difference between the two creatures – the dinosaur had a tail which was more than six feet long. The functional anatomist can only read into such a remarkable resemblance the closest similarity of lifestyle. Convergent evolution has led these animals to look alike. In Desmond's words, "they have come to look like one another because they have come to live like one another." The conclusion is that struthiomimus behaved similarly to Struthio camelus. The ostrich is capable of sustaining speeds of over 45 mph. From its physiology, the dinosaur equivalent looks capable of the same, yet Bakker calculates that if struthiomimus had the constitution of a lizard it would be capable of sustaining hardly two mph!

The kneebones of animals provide another measure of their speed. Fast running creatures have strong muscles attached to the knee to snap the leg straight to provide much of the thrust while running. A protrusion at the knee, the knee crest, is the point of attachment of these muscles. Fast runners have larger muscles and need a stronger knee crest to withstand the stresses. Elephants are large animals with big muscles but they do not run at more than 22 mph. Their knee crests are relatively small.

Similar arguments can be used for the ceratopsian dinosaurs like triceratops, the plated three horned dinosaur looking much like a rhinoceros. These animals were herbivorous and with their powerful armor one might be forgiven for thinking they had no need to run fast. Today the rhino which occupies the same ecological niche is able to run at 30 mph even though it has no natural predators. But the ceratopsians had genuine reason to be able to run fast – they were sought as a nourishing feast by the voracious tyrannosaurus rex. Sure enough, both the prehistoric creature and the modern one have pronounced knee crests and triceratops can be assumed to have moved as fast as the rhinoceros.

What of predators? The arch enemy of the horned dinosaurs, the tyrannosaurs, had exceptionally large knee crests suggestive of a speed of 40 mph. McNeil Alexander's formula supports this view indicating that some types, especially of smaller bipedal dinosaurs, did reach speeds of 40 mph.

Quite fascinating is the deinonychus, the eight feet long carnivorous dinosaur, living in the early part of the Cretaceous period, discovered in 1964 by John Ostrom. Ostrom describes his find as being "a fleet-footed, highly predacious, extremely agile and very active animal, sensitive to many stimuli and quick in its responses. These indicate an unusual level of activity for a reptile and suggest an unusually high metabolic rate." The interesting features of this dinosaur were:

- its legs were long marking it as a fast predator;
- marks on the backbones, reminiscent of those in ostriches, were channels for ligaments which held the spine horizontally as it ran;
- parts of its vertebrae had grown to lengths of about 18 inches and functioned as struts to brace the tail rigid when deinonychus gave chase;
- its feet had three toes but only two of them were used for running, the third having become adapted as a villainous hook for gouging its prey;
- its arms were long and its hands ideally suited to grabbing hold of its victims.

Plainly, deinonychus hunted by giving chase to its intended victim, caught hold of it using its highly developed hands then struck at it with its vicious claw. In so doing it had to balance on its other foot with its tail as a counterpoise to keep its balance. It must have borne some resemblance to the cassowary, a most dangerous modern ground bird weighing 200 pounds. The cassowary also has a large hind claw with which it strikes its enemies using the full power of its strong thigh muscles. Considering that there is reason to believe deinonychus might have been feathered, the resemblance could have been closer than one might initially imagine. We shall have more to say about this remarkable creature later.

The large long-necked dinosaurs such as brontosaurus and diplodocus have also been put through the sawmill of prejudice. It was felt that creatures weighing around 50 tons could not live on dry land. Water was needed to support such a bulk. The experts began to reconstruct them as long-necked crocodiles, their legs, like lizards', splayed on either side of their body. Early reconstructions of dinosaurs such as those at Crystal Palace in South London, England, looked crocodilian. Yet the earliest restorations had given the brontosaurus massive columnar legs like an elephant's.

Nowadays physicists would agree that the thrust of the weight of huge bodies on dry land must be transmitted directly to the ground through sturdy, straight limbs. Weight is related to volume which increases as the cube of the linear dimensions. The strength of the limbs however depends upon their cross section which increases only as the square of the linear dimension. As the weight of a body increases, its supports, its legs, have to thicken at a faster rate. Large terrestrial animals have to have legs like tree stumps.

If the legs were splayed like a lizard's so that, on dry land, the body weight was suspended between the limbs rather than supported directly by them, the animal would be unable to raise itself from the ground without breaking its own legs. Such a reconstruction would have required the sauropods to be purely aquatic. The "crocodile" theorists accepted that the creatures sometimes had to move on land. But that was no problem to them – the sauropods must have slithered through the swamps in which they lived. Blindness! The experts had lizards in their heads and could see nothing else. Sauropods manifestly had a differently shaped thorax from a crocodile precluding them from walking on splayed legs. The deep rib cage of the diplodocus would have required it either to "slither" in a deep trench to make space for its thorax or to slide along on its chest with its legs protruding sideways making little or no contact with the ground. Pillar-like legs supporting the heavy body on top was the only rational reconstruction for the sauropods.

The discovery of brontosaurus tracks at Glen Rose in Texas in 1938 settled the controversy. The stride of the monster was twelve feet but the left and right prints were separated width-ways by only six feet. Brontosaurus made footprints much closer together than a crocodile of equivalent size. Its legs were upright not splayed.

Such large animals must have needed vast amounts of internal energy simply to keep them on their feet. How could they have processed the huge quantities of food required by their high metabolisms when it must have been of fairly low grade and they had relatively small heads?

"Paleontologists usually dismiss any thinking about the soft parts of dinosaurs" because innards do not fossilize. "All speculation about gastrointestinal tracts in the Dinosauria is futile," mocks Bakker, mimicking the orthodox thinkers. Because the sauropods were supposedly partly aquatic, had small heads and had weak teeth, orthodoxy dictated that their diet was soft – duckweed or algae. But is it reasonable to believe that these 50 ton animals had to live off duckweed or algae? Surely a huge maw in a huge head like a baleen whale would be needed for them to scoop up enough algae to sustain such huge bulk. It must be more reasonable to assume that these dinosaurs were terrestrial browsers and ground their food in gizzards or fermented it in their stomachs or both. Modern birds have no teeth and do no chewing but they process often tough food perfectly effectively in their gizzards, and modern ruminants like cows and sheep predigest poor quality grasses by fermentation in their pre-stomachs to prepare it for further mastication.

Birds like ostriches, though they have small heads and long necks similar to many dinosaurs, have both gizzards and fermentation processes to maximize absorbed energy. This compensates for the slow food intake implied by their small heads whilst maintaining their high metabolic rate. Brontosaurs most certainly did the same, and, in fact, their gizzard stones, worn smooth by grinding, have been found.

If dinosaurs were warm-blooded and especially if they were naked, they would have had to grow quickly or die of heat loss. Immature dinosaurs are rarely found. Maturity must have been reached quickly and early growth must have been rapid. Birds and mammals, today's warm-blooded animals, grow to maturity quickly. From a hatchling, an ostrich grows 150 pounds to adulthood in only nine months and an Alsatian dog is twenty times bigger at a year than it was at birth. (Humans are the exception, maturing slowly because of the time needed for them to fill their outsize brains with experience.)

Lizards have quite a different pattern of growth. They do not have a spurt of growth when young but increase in size constantly throughout their lives. Reptiles such as turtles and crocodiles take about ten times longer in the wild to put on the same weight as mammals. The fossil record does not sustain such a growth pattern for dinosaurs. As bone grows it is supported by fibres of the protein, collagen. Fast growing bone has a random pattern of collagen fibres, rather like a felted fabric, whereas slow growing bone has a much more regular pattern of collagen put down in layers. The texture of all dinosaur bone is the irregular type typical of fast growth and warm blood.

Reconstructions like those at Crystal Palace in London depicted all dinosaurs as quadrupeds. Yet in the middle of the 19th century Thomas Huxley realized that some of the dinosaurs were bipedal. The discovery of excellent fossil skeletons of the iguanodon settled the matter. Iguanodons were large erect herbivores 35 feet in length. Their front limbs were much smaller than the massive rear limbs showing they could not have been used for support and evidently were used for grasping branches as the great beasts browsed the trees.

The carnivore, tyrannosaurus rex, was so bipedal that its forelimbs had atrophied until they were apparently quite useless. They consisted of two claws which were too short to reach the creature's mouth and so could not even have been used for feeding. Their purpose, it is surmised, was to provide leverage to lift the monster back on to its legs after it had been resting on its stomach. Their tail however was important, stretching out backwards to provide a counterbalance to the creature's trunk when it moved. These dinosaurs lunged forwards with a sort of waddling effect as the tail swung from side to side. Ancient tracks confirm this picture.

T. rex was an eight ton monster. For it to stand on two limbs, was an effort that required a large amount of energy. Its head was so massive, unlike that of its earlier predecessor, allosaurus, that it needed enormous amounts of energy just to carry it. Is it feasible that such a creature could have had the defective physiological system and intermittent metabolism of a cold-blooded lizard?

One concludes from all this evidence that dinosaurs could not have had the physical make up of present day lizards. They were not just lumbering beasts (though some had a lumbering lifestyle like some mammals), they were sophisticated creatures that kept mammals suppressed for over 100 million years!

There are, of course, counter arguments. Nicholas Hotton III of the Smithsonian Institute claims that 80 per cent of mammals are smaller than the smallest dinosaur, claimed to weigh about 20 pounds. Only two per cent of modern mammals are heavier than two tons but 50 per cent of dinosaurs were. Bulk must have been advantageous to the dinosaurs. The reason claimed is that they had no internal mechanism for maintaining a steady temperature and had to retain their heat by being bulky. A large body loses heat more slowly than a small one because it has less surface area per unit volume. It is the volume that holds the heat and the surface area that loses it. The greater the volume compared with the surface area, the greater the retention of heat. In technical terms, they were mass homeotherms. By growing to huge size they kept a more or less constant temperature giving them many of the characteristics of warm-bloodedness.

Hotton concluded that the dinosaurs had reduced their dependence on the temperature of the environment at a much lower cost than mammals. "The activity of dinosaurs was more sedate than that of mammals. The basic strategy of dinosaurs in general was 'slow and steady', and what it lacked in mammalian elan, it made up in economy."

Yet this solution still leaves us with puzzles. Some dinosaurs "grew no bigger than rabbits or crows": archaeopteryx was no bigger than a crow and compsognathus was no bigger than a chicken. Alan Charig of London's Natural History Museum states that the smallest dinosaur was "no bigger than a mistle thrush", weighing only a few grams. Pterosaurs were even smaller – some were tiny. How could a dinosaur the size of a thrush, or even a chicken, maintain an even temperature and how could hatchlings survive? Both would have a large surface area to volume ratio and would radiate heat rapidly. Baby dinosaurs and pterosaurs could hardly have been other than genuinely warm-blooded, (mass homeotherms without the mass?) Why otherwise did some pterosaurs, if not all, have fur?

Fur is an insulator. It makes no sense for an animal to have fur unless it wants to keep heat in, implying internal heat generation and warm-bloodedness. If a small mammal had no insulation it would need to generate so much heat from its own activity to replace heat lost from its skin that it could never rest. If it did it would cool down, become comatose, be unable to forage and would starve to death. Small mammals need fur to live. Most pterosaurs were not bulky enough to be mass homeotherms. Yet, since they had evolved fur, they must have been warm-blooded. Their large eyes and brains also imply an active lifestyle, a characteristic of warm-blooded animals.

Archaeopteryx, the evolutionary link between dinosaurs and birds, was discovered because it was feathered. Feathers, like fur, act as an insulator suggesting that archaeopteryx had some reason to keep heat in – it was warm-blooded. Yet we noted above it was only as big as a crow, apparently counting out mass homeothermy. Its descendants, the birds, are hotter blooded than mammals. Yet archaeopteryx was living 140 million years ago, right in the middle of the dinosaurs' reign. Is it reasonable to imagine that archaeopteryx had evolved warm-blood when the other dinosaurs were still tinkering with mass homeothermy or, according to many, were cold-blooded reptiles.

Moreover archaeopteryx was not the only feathered dinosaur. A fossil dinosaur discovered in the Gobi Desert named avimimus (bird mimic) was described in 1980 by a Dr Kurzanov. Looking somewhat like compsognathus, a sort of miniature allosaur, the main feature about this dinosaur was that it showed signs of being feathered like archaeopteryx yet is much later, coming from the Late Cretaceous about 75 million years ago. The upper arm bone had low projections like those of birds for the attachment of flight muscles while the lower forelimb had a bony ridge similar to bony protrusions on the forearm of birds. The feathering was thought by Kurzanov to indicate warm-bloodedness especially as they were small. Interestingly the skeleton had no tail making it look particularly bird like.

Unless feathers evolved twice this could be evidence that all small therapods were feathered for insulation. Certainly deinonychus was so similar to archaeopteryx that Bakker presumes it too must have been feathered. Possibly many others also were, though the feathers would not have been flight feathers but rather a sort of down. If small dinosaurs were warm-blooded they could not have evolved without insulation.

As in many disputes, not least scientific ones, the answer might not be at either of the extremes. One could argue that not all the dinosaur genera were fully warm-blooded. The huge, noble sauropods might have been stately homeotherms, needing less internally generated heat, because their bulk retained it. Natural selection in animals like these might have pushed them to vast bulks. Smaller dinosaurs and perhaps predators were warm-blooded. But this idea is not supported by the absence of mass homeothermy today. If it offers such an evolutionary advantage over warm bloodedness, except for tiny animals, why are there no large mass homeotherms in the tropical regions where conditions are stable and ideally suited to them. The large animals are elephants, rhinoceroses and hippopotamuses – fully hot-blooded mammals.

Mass homeotherms must necessarily have been displaced by creatures that were actively warm-blooded irrespective of size. A ten degree Celsius drop in temperature approximately halves the rate of a chemical reaction including those that make the metabolism work. Consequently the activity of a cold-blooded animal roughly halves with every ten degree Celsius drop in temperature. That is why cold-blooded lizards get less active in colder temperatures. In cold climates only the animal with a body temperature regulated at the optimum level for its metabolism can keep active. Closer to the poles or up mountains a temperature must be reached where the mass homeotherms would lose body heat becoming less active whereas a fully warm blooded animal with its built in thermostat would remain active. In some such environment the warm-bloods would have had the advantage over the mass homeotherms.

Over millennia, the advantage of always being active would translate into total dominance. As Robert Bakker puts it: "In direct confrontation, high metabolism always conquers low metabolism." A Bakker cartoon illustrates this idea wonderfully gruesomely in his book, "The Dinosaur Heresies". The cartoon depicts a large sauropod, the mass homeotherm, comatose and unresponsive in the freezing rain, failing to notice tiny rat-like mammals, active despite the cold, eating him alive from the tip of his tail.

It never really occurred, of course. Dinosaurs were quite capable of surviving in freezing climates near both Poles. In 1987 a group of scientists led by Elisabeth Brouwers of the US Geological Survey reported in the journal "Science" that they had found dinosaur remains inside the Arctic Circle. A mixture of young, old, large and small dinosaurs were found near the Colville River. How could cold-blooded dinosaurs or even mass homeotherms survive here in the cold and darkness of winter – they had to be warm-blooded Migration after the fashion of the caribou is just a possibility but again implies a highly active animal. Dinosaur fossils have also been found in Australia which in the Triassic period was much closer to the South Pole having just broken away from Antarctica. Mass homeotherms seem unlikely to have lived in such places.

Furthermore, if dinosaurs were anything other than warm-blooded they could never have displaced the mammals, or rather the mammal-like reptiles,

200 million years ago and could only have survived by taking the role of our mainly small, present day reptiles. That they conquered and then suppressed the mammals, growing eventually to huge size shows that they were fully warm-blooded and not mass homeotherms.

A species evolves to fit different niches in its environment by the process of adaptive radiation. The speed of adaptive radiation depends upon the metabolism of the animal. Cold-blooded animals evolve more slowly than warm-blooded ones. Yet the dinosaurs on several occasions evolved explosively. In one small locality in the US, seven genera of hadrosaurs appeared in only ten million years, all plainly evolved from a known ancestor. Such rates of adaptive radiation have been typical of mammals since the extinction of the dinosaurs.

Evolution is now believed to occur in spurts separated by periods of stability when a species does not change much. This idea, proposed by Eldredge and Gould, was anticipated by an English paleontologist, Hugh Falconer who died in 1866, only seven years after the publication of Darwin's theory. But by the time the arguments of the scientists against the religious bigots had been won the soft voice of Falconer had been forgotten and his message was not heard again until a century after his death.

The periods of equilibrium of species vary according to whether the animal is warm- or cold-blooded. Cold-blooded animals remain stable longer and evolve into new species much less often than warm-blooded ones. The reason is that the higher metabolism of warm-blooded creatures accentuates the competitiveness between them. The evolution of a new species changes the environment of the others which induces them to evolve in response. A positive feedback encouraging rapid evolution occurs and only warm-blooded animals can adapt so quickly. Dinosaurs speciated at a rate comparable with the mammals and birds, not their supposed role models, the reptiles.

An analogy might be a boxer who finds himself champion at a time when there are few contenders and they are of poor quality. He could remain champion for a long time. If there were more and better aspirants for the title, his reign would be shorter. The champion cold-blooded boxer remains champion for longer than does the champion warm-blooded boxer because there is a steady stream of new warm-blooded contenders but few cold-blooded ones. Where the warm and cold-blooded animals are in direct competition the cold-blooded one stands little chance. If a human boxer were fearful that one day he might leave the ring dead, he might be very glad to opt out of boxing and chose instead the life of a grocer or a publican. In a sense, that is what the cold-blooded animals that have survived till today have done. They have opted out of direct competition with the warm-bloods.

If the broader classifications of genera and families are considered instead of species, the differences in rates of adaptation are enhanced. Taxonomic families of genera are even more likely to be long lived. Indeed families of cold-blooded species often seem to go on indefinitely. The family of modern crocodiles has survived for a hundred million years and, according to Bakker, the average for cold-blooded reptiles is 55 million years. If dinosaurs were cold-blooded their taxonomic families should survive for a similar length of time. But "the dinosaurs evolved quickly, changed repeatedly, and turned out wave after wave of new species with new adaptations all through their reign," according to Bakker. The average life of a family of dinosaurs was only 25 million years, virtually the same as that of families of mammals.

Desmond wrote: "Nobody before [Bakker and Ostrom] had demonstrated the inextricable relationship between high metabolism, stable temperature and erect posture, yet once explicitly stated this linking seemed obvious and natural. It resolved the long-standing contradictions inherent in the ludicrous sun-basking brontosaur model by scrapping the model altogether and substituting an endothermic dinosaur... The dinosaur's suspected high metabolism and fast energy production places it not with cold-blooded lizards but warmer-blooded mammals and birds."

Let us scotch another fallacy: that the mammals were superior to the dinosaurs and succeeded by out-competing them. Both mammals and dinosaurs evolved from earlier types at about the same time in the Triassic, about 200 million years ago, but it was the dinosaurs that established their superiority and for the next 140 million years mammals had to be content with harsh ecological niches that the dinosaurs could not occupy. The fossil record testifies to the superiority of dinosaurs over mammals for twice the period that mammals have dominated the earth. Only when the dinosaurs mysteriously disappeared 65 million years ago did the mammals have the chance to succeed.

The story is quite amazing.

The mammals' ancestors, the therapsids, had actually ruled the earth for 30 million years before the arrival of the dinosaurs. Then in a pre-historic world war they lost to the antecedents of the dinosaurs. Dinosaurs were not cold-blooded, as we have seen, but evidently not even dinosaurs were the first warm-blooded animals. Warm-blood evolved at some point in the 120 million years that therapsids and their predecessors, the pelycosaurs, dominated the earth. Not only are mammals warm blooded, their predecessors were. Not only were dinosaurs warm blooded, their predecessors were too.

The dimetrodon, a predatory pelycosaur was cold-blooded. It had a fin on its back probably for more efficient heat exchange between the animal and its surroundings. It would have turned this vane fully towards the sun when the animal wanted to be warmer and edge on to the sun or into the breeze when it wanted to be cooler. Capillary blood vessels in the fin then allowed the blood to heat up or cool down very effectively. It was a more efficient way of doing what lizards do today and surely would have been retained by later generations. It might also have served as a sexual signal to attract mates rather like the salamander's tail. As we shall see sexual selection tends to enhance characteristics and such a sexual signal would be expected to be favored by subsequent evolution. Remembering that cold-blooded creatures evolve slowly, the fin looked destined for a long life. Yet the dimetrodon's descendants had lost it. Why did it disappear so quickly? The answer could be that this was the point at which warm blood evolved.

If the fin were a heat exchanger, dimetrodon's warm-blooded descendants had no need of it having developed a more efficient method of temperature control. A signalling device implies a passive approach to sex but with the evolution of warm-blood active courtship (like the rutting of stags) had probably replaced the older passive form. The therapsids, undoubtedly used active methods of gaining sexual dominance, like head butting, which required surplus energy compared with that used by the earlier animals and which showed they were warm-blooded. The dinosaurs used both active and passive sexual strategies giving them a variety of courtships similar to that seen today among mammals and birds, both warm-blooded.

The pelycosaurs survived essentially unchanged for about 20 million years but then were replaced in only a few million years by the therapsids, mammal-like reptiles which eventually evolved into mammals. Relevant here is the evidence Bakker found for warm-bloodedness in predator:prey ratios. A warm-blooded animal needs a lot more energy than a cold-blooded one so a warm-blooded predator needs to kill more prey to supply it. A given number of prey animals of a given size will support a smaller number of warm-blooded predators than cold-blooded ones. The metabolic rate of the predators can be deduced from predator:prey ratios which can therefore give us an idea of when a more active metabolism and warm blood evolved.

The pelycosaur predator, dimetrodon, had a variety of prey and was often the most common animal in its environment, an unusual situation, the food chain usually narrowing towards the top. Its predator:prey ratio was 1:4, more or less the same as that of the wolf spider (naturally cold-blooded) and its prey. The predator:prey ratios of therapsids were typically about 1:14 indicating a significant move to warm-bloodedness. By comparison, Eocene mammals show a ratio of about 1:30 and modern mammals of 1:100 or even less. But mankind has reduced the equilibrium numbers of predators so much that modern ratios are grossly untypical and the value for mammals in favorable environments is around 1:25 – which is just the ratio found for the dinosaurs.

The predator:prey ratio for therapsids indicated a marked move towards warm-blood and indeed the explosive adaptive radiation with which they replaced the pelycosaurs is typical of the warm-bloods. The therapsids' own rate of speciation matched that of modern mammals. The earliest therapsids suffered a mass extinction after about ten million years and were replaced by new therapsids evolved from the old. All the evidence is that these new proto-mammals were warm-blooded. Again after a few million years they suffered a mass extinction and a fresh group of therapsids took over including the large cynodonts, with remarkably dog-like skulls and the herbivorous dicynodonts. Analysis of their fossils confirms that these also were warm-blooded. The external physiology (bumps for muscle attachment like the knee crest) and the internal physiology (bone texture) of therapsid bones point to warm-blood. Walking speeds calculated from fossil footprints were in the warm-blooded range and finally some of the therapsids lived at extreme latitudes where it must have been cool if not cold, making it probable that they had already evolved hair and were looking quite mammal-like.

Rapid cycles of extinctions and repopulation tell us that these animals were warm-blooded – through active competition prone to mass extinction but able to restock the environment with new species by explosive adaptive radiation. Once warm-bloodedness arrived, it stayed. The cold-bloods were never able to gain control again. They evolved too slowly to fill the empty niches created by mass extinctions of the warm-bloods. Even the paleontological establishment accepts that the wolf-headed cynodonts were surely warm-blooded. So if dinosaurs were cold-blooded they could not have replaced them.

You might argue that even in "The Age of the Mammals" a lot of cold-blooded animals like tortoises and snakes have thrived though not as the dominant life form. Couldn't the dinosaurs, though cold-blooded, have done the same, biding their time to eventually wrest control from the pre-mammals. It sounds feasible perhaps, but, though cold-blooded animals remain numerous in the world of the mammals, we saw above that they have occupied specialized niches in which they have avoided direct confrontation with the warm-bloods. Their survival has depended on that.

Tortoises evolved from turtles by adapting for a life on land about 50 million years ago, after the demise of the dinosaurs. On dry land the tortoise was in apparent competition with mammals, also free to occupy empty niches left by the dinosaurs. It succeeded to such an extent that one species called colossochelys grew as big as a small car. But the tortoise was not in direct competition with the mammals! It did not try to out-do the mammals at their own game! Instead it made the best of the qualities that it had – an armored carapace and the infinite patience conferred upon it by its slow, cold-blooded metabolism. Harried by a predatory mammal the tortoise, like a feudal baron, withdrew into its keep, pulled up the drawbridge and settled down to withstand the siege. And the tortoise could wait a lot longer than any mammal. The colossochelys survived for millions of years until recent times, able to withstand anything mammals could come up with – until they invented man. The intelligent mammal realized that not only was the giant tortoise helpless on its back but it also carried with it a conveniently large stewpot. Groups of men were soon levering the tortoises on to their backs and building bonfires underneath them. The result is that no colossochelys remains in the world today.

There are about as many species of snake living on the land as there are mammals. Snakes are predators but ones that, like the herbivorous tortoises, make the most of their own special features including the infinite patience of the cold-bloods. The snake is able to poise unseen, because of its unusually extended shape, and totally motionless, because of its cold-blooded metabolism, until some careless victim stumbles upon it, whereupon it is swiftly poisoned or more slowly constricted. Snakes make the most of what they have and do not actively compete with warm-blooded mammals.

Yet during the Triassic period the confrontation between the mammal-like reptiles and the forerunners of the dinosaurs was head on. In Bakker's words, "a titanic ecological battle was waged between the advanced pre-mammals, led by the dicynodonts and the cynodonts, and the Erythrosuchidae [crimson crocodiles, early predecessors of the crocodiles and dinosaurs] and their descendants... Two mighty evolutionary dynasties collided in direct competition."

What happened? The fastest and most efficient predators of the early Triassic, the warm-blooded cynodonts and their therapsid kin, lost to the supposedly cold-blooded crimson crocodiles and to their descendants, the thecodonts. The only relatives of the therapsids surviving till today are the duck-billed platypus and the spiny anteater. Significantly enough these animals are only partly warm-blooded. A platypus's typical body temperature is only 30 degrees Celsius, compared with 37 degrees Celsius for most mammals, and it is subject to wide fluctuations. It also lays eggs and has no nipples but instead has refined sweat glands that ooze milk into its fur for the neonate to lick. It is just what one might expect from a form intermediate between reptiles and mammals.

The therapsids probably became warm-blooded to protect themselves against the advent of colder conditions. Then, for the same reason they developed a furry exterior. But why did the crimson crocodiles and thecodonts become warm-blooded? The answer seems to be precisely because they were adapting for an active, bipedal mode of living – and, as we have seen that would not have been possible without internal heat regulation.

Thecodonts evolved from swamp dwelling forms which developed strong rear limbs for swimming and steering themselves in the water, just like frogs and crocodiles. The swamps began to dry up in the middle of the Triassic period and many of a previous dominant life form, the amphibians, died out. The thecodonts' ancestors were somewhat more adaptable, necessarily learning to spend more time out of the water until they became independent of it. On dry land they found that their strong hind limbs allowed them to rear up and catch the insects that lived in profusion around the drying swamps. They found that they could run on their hind legs for short distances, improving their chances of survival. Simultaneously, through natural selection, they became warm-blooded thereby gaining the energy needed for running and hunting. Finally they brought their legs into a better position beneath their bodies to provide more efficient propulsion to exploit their faster metabolism. With long hind legs and an energy system to match, the thecodonts were ready to take on the world.

Thus the thecodonts ousted the therapsids from their advantageous position. They, in turn, were to succumb. The dinosaurs proper, descendants of the thecodonts, appeared on the scene by the end of the Triassic. The invasion of the thecodonts and their successors, the dinosaurs, put paid to the ambitions of the mammal's precursors, the therapsids, and those also of the mammals themselves for a hundred million years or so.

Dinosaurs did not appear until 200 million years after the first vertebrates crawled on to the land. As we have seen, they were preceded by a series of other types of land animals including a period of several tens of million years about 250 million years ago when the pre-mammals dominated. They were warm-blooded but they were not the first warm-blooded animals. They were the culmination of a series of mighty dynastic struggles among previous warm-bloods. Bipedalism and possibly superior lungs gave them an advantage that others, including the mammals, could not match. In only five million years, short in geological terms, the dinosaurs sprinted to power. It has taken about five million years from the emergence of mankind to world dominance!

For 140 million years mammals were forced into less desirable habitats especially where it was cold and barren. They lived in burrows, terrified of the dinosaurs and pterosaurs. Insignificance was an advantage. Tiny creatures like shrews and mice were less likely to attract attention. Because mammals at this time were very small – the largest was no bigger than a hedgehog – and rocky terrain is not suitable for fossilization, fossilized remains of these mammals are uncommon. Only their tiny teeth are commonly found. Though small and insignificant, mammals were not free from danger. By day, though large dinosaurs would not have been interested in them, the smaller predatory dinosaurs were. And besides dinosaurs, true lizards were still sunning themselves motionlessly on the rocks waiting for a small animal to come unwarily by. Mammals were nocturnal. They had to forage by night when it was too cold for lizards to be active, limiting their enemies to small nocturnal dinosaurs.

The mammals' niche was quite lowly for the millions of years of the supremacy of the dinosaur. They could not compete with a superior animal. All was changed by the mass extinctions which ended the Cretaceous age. The mammals inherited the earth and eventually one of their species came to do remarkable things. It was the thinking mammal – mankind.

HDM 1988

Exhibit 3. Central American Basilisk lizard running bipedally

CHAPTER FOUR

A THINKING MAMMAL...

"Darwinian Man, though well behaved,
At best is only a monkey shaved!"

W.S.Gilbert

The story told by Don Johanson about the discovery of Lucy aptly illustrates the fallibility of the experts. Like Ostrom's colleagues who missed deinonychus, Johanson's so easily overlooked a find which proved to be astounding. Lucy is the name Johanson gave to the fossil remains of an early hominid later shown to be some four million years old. The skeletal fragments were of a female and, when the prospectors returned to camp to tell of their discovery, a tape recorder was playing the Beatles' recording of "Lucy in the Sky with Diamonds". And so the remains were christened "Lucy".

Johanson had woken that day feeling that "something terrific might happen" and, although pressed by organizational and bureaucratic work, he had agreed to go with a young graduate student, Tom Gray, to show him a site called Locality 162. After four hours on site they were beginning to get tired in the hot Ethiopian sun. Still feeling lucky, Johanson determined to take a quick look at a small gully that had already been expertly surveyed no less than twice by other members of the expedition.

The pair were just about to leave when Johanson casually said to Gray, "look, that's a bit of hominid arm." One of the most significant finds in human prehistory had been made and on a site that had already been thoroughly surveyed, just because a young and relatively inexperienced team leader had a hunch and felt lucky.

Lucy is the most complete ancient human skeleton yet discovered. She was 40 per cent complete, an hominid, that is an erect walking primate (her pelvis had fully adapted to the upright stance), only about four feet tall but full grown. In fact she must have been aged at least 20 because her wisdom teeth had erupted fully. Her head looked primitive and her brain was not much bigger than a chimpanzee's with a volume of about 400 cm^3. She was a four feet high ape with a human looking body but underdeveloped skull and brain.

The human race obviously still had a long way to come in the four million years between then and now, but Lucy already showed clear distinctions from the other apes. The shape of her hip bones and her upright posture signal Lucy (or Australopithecus afarensis, to use the scientific name) as being closer to us than the chimpanzee, the closest living relative of man. Though the difference between humans and chimpanzees is only about one per cent according to protein and DNA matching, the physiological and cultural differences are astonishing. Skeletal structure and posture, skin, muscles, brain, intelligence, speech, ability to make tools and social organization all differ remarkably for such close relatives, showing that humans have differentiated themselves very distinctly from other apes, including Lucy, in a puzzlingly short time. What difference of habitat or experience initiated these changes from the ancestral common stock, and what continued them after her? These are admittedly difficult questions to answer but perhaps an examination of the history of the primates, the mammalian order to which we belong, from the demise of the dinosaurs to the present time will yield some clues.

The very name "primates" betrays our self-centered view of the world. The order of primates is the first, the prime order, because we are in it. It comprises some 200 species whose characteristic features are binocular vision and grasping hands.

Some of the diminutive mammals rather like shrews that inhabited the earth during the time of the dinosaurs took to the shrub and then, at about the time of the dinosaurs' death, to the trees to become the forerunners of the primates. These early arboreal mammals were insectivores needing to grasp and move quickly while not falling from the branches. By about 55 million years ago, they had developed the primate grasping hand with its nails instead of claws and a partly opposable thumb. Hands reduced the need for a snout with which to explore, and reduced the need for teeth – jaws became smaller. Their short snout and large, widely spaced eyes meant that vision was more important than smell. To catch insects efficiently and to leap accurately they had evolved binocular vision. The field of view from both eyes overlapped giving them a three dimensional view of the world so that they could accurately judge distance. The movement of the eyes to the front of the skull allowed the braincase and therefore the brain to enlarge.

The ancestor of the primates would have looked rather like the tarsier or, more so, the curious, primitive tupaia of South East Asia. The tarsier has immense eyes for its size (it is nocturnal) but its other features are plainly primate. The tupaia has long separable fingers but no opposable thumb and therefore has no grasp. It has claws instead of nails. It has large eyes but their fields of vision do not fully overlap. It has a snout and a keen sense of smell, and it lives mainly on the ground, though sometimes it runs up trees like a squirrel. From such a creature evolved the prosimians, the pre-monkeys, of which the lemurs are one group.

Through continental drift, Madagascar split from Africa about 55 million years ago and carried with it the primates then living there. Those left behind on the African mainland evolved into monkeys and the rest of the primate line but in Madagascar lesser changes took place. Pressure of competition was less keen and Madagascan lemurs remained essentially unchanged until today, although they did adapt to a variety of ecological niches.

The Madagascan ring tailed lemur has grasping hands with opposable thumbs and nails not claws. Their babies use their hands to cling tenaciously to their mothers. It has binocular vision, it is social and attentive to its offspring, but, on the ground, it walks on all fours. Another Madagascan lemur, the sifaka, can stand on two legs but cannot walk – it leaps along the ground as if it were leaping from branch to branch.

Meanwhile, on the mainland of Africa, about 40 million years ago monkeys evolved, derived it seems from ancestors that split from the lemurs much earlier. Their success drove the African lemurs into the night – they became nocturnal. All African monkeys are active during the day, and to take advantage of the daylight have evolved color vision, a boon for spotting ripe fruit. However they lost much of their sense of smell, unlike the lemurs. Color vision led to them using brightly colored features to signal their species, their sexual receptivity, and to distinguish friends and enemies. They also became raucous chatterboxes with a varied vocabulary of sounds, important for the emergence of speech.

Primates have tended to increase in size as they evolved. 30 million years ago some primates got too large to walk on all fours on the branches like monkeys and instead took to swinging beneath them – these became the apes. Today's orangutans are the largest tree dwellers. At over 400 pounds they have reached their limit. Gorillas are bigger but they do not swing in trees as adults. A third of adult orangutans have broken bones. As they grow up they must often experience branches breaking under their weight. Adult orangs swing about in the branches of the tree they are already in, because they can feel the strength of the branches as they grip them. But, rather than making a bold swing to the next tree and risking a branch they have not tested, they descend to the ground and walk. The step from monkey to ape required a change in mobility at the shoulder and adaptation of the muscles of the abdomen to the upright rather than horizontal posture.

20 million years ago apes were common – monkeys were rarer. Only from about ten million years ago has the situation reversed. In the intervening period significant changes occurred. The linking of land masses gives an opportunity for evolutionary divergence and it was about 18 million years ago that Africa collided with Eurasia causing a flurry of evolutionary activity. Antelopes, pigs, elephants and rodents have all evolved since then. Part of the reason for this was the evolution of grass from about 24 million years ago, the potential of which was achieved only when the world became colder and more arid 15 million years ago, providing an environment to be exploited by the grazing animals.

David Pilbeam, an Englishman teaching anthropology at Yale, has shown that by ten million years ago there were two major groups of apes, the dryopithecines having apelike teeth, and the ramapithecines, having human-like teeth with reduced canines and a flatter face. If their teeth differentiated dryopithecines and ramapithecines, a significant change of eating habits must have led to their evolutionary separation. Ramapithecus proved a very successful ape, its remains having been found in Europe, Asia and Africa. But despite its teeth, a carefully reconstructed specimen looks too like an orangutan for it to be a sure ancestor of human beings. The teeth remain a puzzle. Why do they look so human? The Taung baby mentioned above was a much later type of ape (later even than Lucy) called Australopithecus africanus or A.africanus for short. Its teeth, says Don Johanson, a teeth and jaws specialist, are "very similar" to those of ramapithecus. Perhaps a link is still possible.

In the four million years separating ramapithecus and Lucy, even the experts speculate unashamedly simply because there is no evidence. Gribbon and Cherfas have suggested that the original brachiating apes, similar to orangutans or gibbons, emerged near the Indus which was then surrounded by dense forest. From there the apes spread out. Some moved Eastward through lush rainforests, ideally suited to them, to Indonesia where they still live relatively unchanged – the orangutan and the gibbon! Others migrated Westward via Arabia into Africa. *They* did not meet such familiar conditions. As they slowly migrated, the forests disappeared through increasing desiccation and the apes found themselves having to spend more time on the ground. By the time they reached Africa they had become knuckle walkers, and eventually chimpanzees and gorillas. Some chose to shelter in what woodland or forest the could find but others adapted to open grassland.

Orthodox savannah theorists believe that the apes were already in Africa but increasing desiccation forced some of the forest apes to adapt to woodland then to open country. A gradation of evolutionary niches were thus occupied by the apes; the apes which stayed behind in the deep forest became today's gorillas, in woodlands were the chimpanzees and on the savannah, man's family, the hominids. The grassland's new visitors lacked the obvious requirements of success on the plains, being slow, unarmored, relatively weak and without claws or powerful teeth, unlike their competitors already there, but they survived and had made the transition by the time of Lucy. They must have had some advantages. What were they? Are they factors in the growth of intelligence?

Desmond Clark has put forward one intriguing speculation based on tentative evidence. He found burnt tree stumps associated with remains of fossil hominids four million years old. Did Lucy's contemporaries already use fire, keeping flame going by keeping tree stumps alight as farmers do today in India? If the answer is "yes", fire could have been the vital factor that allowed hominids to move on to the savannah without having to fear predators. Domesticating fire might have been the essential step to humanity, and it might have happened very early on. A thought which must be regarded as not yet proven.

Other advantages were more evident: their binocular vision; their manipulative hands able to grasp a branch or a stone; their brachiating arms giving them the ability to brandish sticks and to throw stones; their well developed brains. Once on the savannah, lack of the usual specializations for grassland living forced them to compete by using these other advantages and by developing new ones, amongst which was the ability to stand erect. The apes had to be wary, and to use their keen vision to maximum advantage they had to stretch to their full height to look out for approaching cats or hyenas. They took to walking bipedally, a habit which then proved to have other advantages. Hands and arms were permanently freed to grasp and wield the natural weapons that lay about and to allow the apes to change and improve those weapons.

Groups of the new savannah creatures could, with the aid of stones and sticks, keep off dangerous predators. They also found that, with stones they could stun and maim at a distance. A well thrown stone is a remarkably good weapon. As Richard Leakey puts it, "the extraordinary ability of modern humans to throw objects with force and with astonishing accuracy, even at moving targets is interesting... The brain mechanisms that underlie this unique accomplishment may have their evolutionary roots in the hunting activities of Homo erectus," (the variety of man that went before us). The sort of skill Leakey means can be seen on the cricket field and the baseball diamond where outfielders can place the ball with amazing precision even from distances of 60 or 70 yards.

Having learned a variety of hunting skills, meat would have given the savannah apes an additional advantage because the energy and protein of meat is concentrated. But the gathering of fruit, roots, berries, grubs, insects and fungus would have continued to provide their basic needs.

In the gap in the fossil record between ramapithecus and Lucy when did the forest and savannah apes separate? Differences in DNA show that mankind is more closely related to the chimpanzees, the common chimp and the pygmy chimp, than the other great apes. Man is the third species of chimpanzee, or alternatively, chimpanzees are two other species of men. They differ less in DNA than do some populations of the same species. The three parted company with their next closest relative, the gorillas, about nine million years ago. Carl Linnaeus, the founder of modern taxonomy, classified mankind into a special category. Regretting his decision later, he said, "if I had called man an ape, or vice versa, I would have fallen under the ban of all the ecclesiastics. It may be that as a naturalist I should have done so." Had Linnaeus had the courage to defy the churchmen, we might now be less anthropocentric, more humble and have more empathy with the other inhabitants of the planet.

I noted above that Sarich and Wilson found mankind and the chimpanzees to have separated as little as five million years ago. More unusual evidence of the date of our separation from the apes comes from DNA studies of the herpes virus. Herpes simplex causes cold sores and genital warts in primates. Though a single species, it exists in humans as two races each with its own preferred site for colonization. In the other apes, it exists as only one variety and does not mind whether it is introduced to the oral or the genital region.

Why are there two herpes races for humans but only one for the other apes? Herpes is only transmitted by intimate contact – in the apes by sexual contact. Female apes are only in oestrus occasionally and male apes, like many other mammals, use their noses and tongues to determine when the female is becoming receptive. The virus has plenty of opportunity to get from one orifice to the other. Human females however are receptive all the time. The male has no need of a test for oestrus. Kissing became the main show of interest and affection. Human behavior cut down the opportunities for the virus to swap sites. Over several million years the virus has begun to evolve into separate species, one suited to genital transmission and one suited to oral transmission. Speciation is not yet complete possibly because oral sex, though serving no obvious purpose, is still indulged in by some humans for pleasure, an evolutionary anachronism.

An American team of microbiologists have used the molecular clock to date the human herpes virus to somewhere between 7.5 and 10.7 million years ago. This is earlier than the more direct estimate of the antiquity of mankind but ties in well with the gap between ramapithecus and Lucy when the human line probably separated. Possibly, the apes' behavior patterns were changing before the separation of the hominids occurred so that the emergence of the herpes races pre-dated it.

Interpolating as best we can, the hominids appeared perhaps seven million years ago, near the start of the gap in the fossil record which lasts until the time of Lucy (A.afarensis).

Not all hominids were man's ancestors. Some apes that made the transition from the woodlands (or evolved from the ones that did) failed to learn how to make stone tools and became extinct. Johanson and White regard A.afarensis as ancestral to Homo, the species of men, and also to A.africanus and A.robustus, the extinct lines. The Homo branch split off about three million years ago and the result was ourselves. The Australopithecine line proved a dead end when africanus evolved into the more specialized robustus. This became extinct about a million years ago possibly because of the unwelcome attentions of hungry Homo, and competition in the same ecological niche from some monkeys, which, faced with the same problems as our ape ancestors about four million years ago, moved to open country, sleeping in trees and caves. They were baboons.

Walking upright preceded any other human traits (kissing would have accompanied this change). A.afarensis stood fully upright but was not regarded by Johanson and White as Homo. If it were then all its descendants, the other upright Australopithecines, including robustus, would also have to be classified as being Homo. The key distinction between the Australopithecines and Homo is that only Homo seems to have made stone tools. Not that the Australopithecines did not use tools. Fairly surely they used what they found about them, perhaps even more so than chimpanzees which use objects found around them as tools and weapons, and can even fashion simple tools by stripping leaves from sticks. But only Homo has left evidence of manufacturing tools, by knapping stones, from about two million years ago onwards. Australopithecine hominids had been around for one or even two million years before tools are found, indicating that they did not invent them.

Not all anthropologists accept these ideas. Some believe that A.africanus is indeed in the human line and did make a very simple stone tool by striking a stone to give it a sharp edge. They argue that this released the brake on the evolution of intelligence and progress speeded up leading to man . Only A.robustus split off into an evolutionary dead end by sticking to a diet largely of fruit and leaves. With this diet they did not need to make tools and eventually, becoming easy meat for their brighter cousins, were hunted to extinction.

According to Johanson and White's hypothesis, Homo and either one or the other of the Australopithecines lived in the same parts of Africa at the same time. Others believe that both A.africanus and A.robustus were contemporaries of early man. Obviously something must have occurred to distinguish such similar species all with the same ancestor and apparently inhabiting the same region at the same time.

Had they been, at some stage, physically separated for long enough for speciation to occur? Or could speciation have occurred without such separation? According to some savannah theorists, natural barriers such as the rift valleys, rivers and mountains of East Africa could have isolated groups of apes for long enough for speciation into the Australopithecines and Homo to occur. The distinctions between them were then maintained through habitat and diet. For other savannah experts, these latter would have been sufficient for speciation without physical separation. In Johanson's view, A.afarensis, an upright ape, differentiated by diet into two races that speciated ultimately into A.robustus, an upright ape, and H.habilis, the first man.

A.robustus had a massive jaw. Its jaw muscles were so large they required a bony ridge along the top of the skull to anchor them. Their teeth were large and smooth. Microscopic examination shows marks similar to those on the teeth of a chimpanzee whose main food is fruit supplemented by a variety of other items such as eggs, ants, small mammals and lizards, but not roots, the grit of which causes deep scratches. The massive jaws, teeth and jaw muscles suggest a bulky diet of low grade food requiring a lot of chewing – probably fruit and leaves.

H.habilis was more omnivorous. Examination of their teeth shows them to be deeply scored like those of a rooting animal. A pig, for example, has scratched teeth from the grit it eats with its diet of roots. Early humans must therefore have taken a lot of grit with their food suggesting roots, meat – probably largely scavenged – and possibly dung. It is humbling to think that we might have set out as eaters of other creatures' faeces! H.habilis used a fairly simple tool consisting of a rounded stone knapped on one side to give a sharp edge. The rounded side was held in the hand while the tool was used for scraping and cutting. Nigel Calder describes H.habilis as "mutant apemen with overgrown heads and an unprecedented ability to enlarge their brains after birth". A modern human baby has a head only the size of an ape but it grows to three times its birth size during childhood, the greatest enlargements being in the region which has to do with solving problems and language. Nevertheless H.habilis brains were only about half the volume of those of modern humans.

Their successors, H.erectus, were hunters not scavengers. They were cleverer and used a hand axe, a stone chipped to a point and held, club-like in the palm. Cutting tools were important to herbivores turned meat eaters. Chimps and baboons, though they might have had the same intellectual potential, did not have the same incentive to make cutting tools as the weak toothed apes. They had no need to invent tools to help them eat meat because their teeth were strong enough. The simplest tools were stone flakes used to cut strips from carcasses. A microscopic examination of stone chips can be used in the same way as a microscopic examination of teeth. It can reveal what materials they have been used on. An examination of stone chips from 1.5 million years ago shows that some were used for meat cutting, some for grass cutting, showing that gathering had become quite sophisticated, and some for wood whittling suggesting the use of wooden tools like wooden spears.

Between 1.5 and one million years ago, Homo erectus, the first true men, definitely used fire. From Homo habilis until the present day teeth have become smaller by 40 per cent mainly through the use of cooking to tenderize meat and vegetables. The increasing diet of meat might have served to distinguish one of the savannah hominids and provided a stimulus for the development of the tools to process it.

With all this manual activity, refinements of the hand and corresponding changes in the centers of the brain coordinating the hand led to Neanderthal man, who reached Europe 600,000 years ago, able to make sophisticated stone tools. Despite the brutal looking drawings of him in many books, Neanderthal man was probably of the same species as us although his bone structure was somewhat heavier. 200,000 years ago he painted the first pictures on the walls of caves. Arguably it is art that truly distinguishes mankind. Though several other animals can use tools of a sort, no other creature can make recognizable images. H.sapiens neanderthalensis were also the first humans to bury their dead with tenderness and ritual. Bodies were laid carefully in their graves and decorated with freshly picked flowers.

But inexorably the human animal continued to evolve into new varieties and about 100,000 years ago Homo sapiens sapiens, anatomically modern man, arrived on the scene in Africa. It was to be another 60,000 years before he made a real impact. By 34,000 years ago Neanderthal man was extinct.

And so we come to civilization. Jericho was the first town with a population of 2000, some 11,000 years ago. Catal Huyuk, in present day Turkey, was the first city, 9000 years ago, with a population of 5000. Cities introduced the diseases of civilization, diseases of overcrowding and insanitation, of stress and pollution – venereal disease, plague, cancer, heart attacks, psychoses and warfare. The modern world had begun.

Mankind, simple hunter gatherers, ate of the fruit of the tree of knowledge, noticed their nakedness and left the Garden of Eden. With their new found knowledge they invented agriculture and had to toil in the earth from dawn till dusk. But they had discovered an economic system that provided for the exponential growth of human population: 10,000 years ago there were less than ten million people in the world; today there are six billion.

This is a long story. It is a remarkable story – remarkably detailed. But is it true? No doubt we can have confidence in the narrative over the last few tens of thousands of years, but what of the previous ten million years?

40 per cent of the skeleton of Lucy was found, an astonishing proportion, for the truth is that everything we know about human evolution depends upon very few remains indeed. Lucy is the only skeleton of a species, likely to be in the line of man, living between 75,000 and 3.5 million years ago, that is anything like complete. The rest of the remains that this construction is based upon are merely fragments – mainly of skulls. Don Johanson and Maitland Edey have noted: "postcranial remains were horribly scarce". David Pilbeam and Stephen J.Gould put it more scathingly, "human paleontology shares a peculiar trait with such disparate subjects as theology and extraterrestrial biology: it contains more practitioners than objects for study".

Baron Cuvier could have felt quite happy about this situation, "we have half of a jawbone... There can be no doubt, the creature looked like this". But maybe some experts today are learning how to be humble. Richard Leakey argued in the Scientific American in 1978 for the need for "caution in the making of taxonomic judgments... when the evidence at hand is a few isolated teeth". Or in the blunt words of Clark Howell, Johanson's teacher, and a most respected anthropologist, "you can't tell a great deal from a single tooth", a direct contradiction of Cuvier's dictum. Not only hominid remains are scarce, so are remains of our cousins the great apes – Johanson tells us that no fossil chimpanzee skull has ever been found. Over the 50 million years from our lemur like ancestors there are only six or seven distinct skulls which can be identified as stages in the evolution of man. Between Lucy of four million years ago and an ape found by David Pilbeam harking from about eight million years ago there is that vast gap in remains.

We see the story of man told on television by polymath television personalities, but their reconstructions of human evolution are largely fantasy – simply because the supporting material has not been found. As Lyall Watson so pictorially points out in "Earthworks", his 1986 book: "all the physical evidence we have for human evolution can be put, with room to spare, into a single coffin". What then of the story of man I have just related? Gribbon and Cherfas in "The Monkey Puzzle," admit, "[though] many ordinary people believe that the riddle of human origins has been solved, in no case is this true, and all the ideas in print today – including our own – are more or less naked speculation".

From all this, students of human evolution have little reason to be dogmatic about their assertions. If their conjectures are accurate, it is not because they are based on unequivocal evidence. As Richard Leakey says with refreshing candor, "we [must] remain fully aware of the dangers of drawing conclusions from evidence that is so incomplete".

The paucity of hominid or prehominid remains contrasts with the richness of the dinosaur remains, perhaps surprisingly since mankind evolved sometime in the most recent ten million years whereas dinosaurs died off 65 million years ago. However our search for the intelligent dinosaur is not made easier for that simply because we are not comparing like with like.

- The period we are looking at for dinosaurs covered some 140 million years compared with about ten million for man's development.
- The term dinosaur covers very many species whereas we are looking specifically for only a few in looking for man's ancestors.
- The geographical distribution of the dinosaurs was virtually the whole world while man's ancestors were localized.
- The population of the dinosaurs was huge while the first men by definition must have been small in numbers.
- Finally, the likelihood of any creature being fossilized depends upon the conditions where it died. Mankind's ancestors, it seems, were not easily fossilized.

Despite an abundance of dinosaur remains compared with remains of human ancestors, there must have been many dinosaurs that lived and left no trace – or very little. At best there may be few fossils of the ones we would like, those ancestral to the intelligent dinosaurs, for the same reasons that there are so few fossils of pre-humans. But there are so few fossils of hominids that our speculations on the evolution of intelligence dinosaurs are scarcely less credible than the anthropologists' on the evolution of mankind.

Don Johanson tells us, "we do not have, even today, an agreed-on definition of humankind, a clear set of specifications that will enable any anthropologist in the world to say quickly and with confidence, 'This is human; that one isn't'". The experts cannot agree. What then does human evolution tell the layman about the features that are singularly human, or are the key to human success? In scrutinizing the evidence for the aquatic phase of human development later in this book, we shall identify a lot of peculiar characteristics humans have that other apes lack. Is just one of them the key to human intellectual development, or is it rather a complex of features?

Mankind's legacy from the primate founder, the small nocturnal tree dweller which survived the disaster of 65 million BC, comprised the grasping fingers and opposable thumb, with nails instead of claws. Later primates added first binocular vision then, when they became diurnal and fruit eaters, color vision. Subsequently they developed in size, intelligence and social behavior diverging to orangutans, gibbons, gorillas, chimpanzees and men (all apes), and baboons (a monkey). The last three are characteristically able to exploit all food available, a catholicity of diet based upon opportunism – the skill of taking whatever is going. Related to this is another important characteristic, highly developed in the primates, curiosity. Curiosity prompts animals to explore new objects especially when young. Higher primates carry this into adulthood enabling them to discover new opportunities that they might learn how to exploit.

These factors, the grasping hand, binocular color vision, an omnivorous diet, curiosity and opportunism might all be important but since our near relatives, the chimpanzees, and some rather more distant relatives, are endowed with them, they cannot be the factors peculiar to human evolution. Humans also have: a constantly upright stance and striding gait uncommon in mammals, bipedalism; a large brain, intelligence; very short, fine hair giving a naked look and very sweaty skin with millions of sweat glands; highly manipulative forelimbs involving coordination of hands and brain; the ability to make sophisticated tools; parents who care for their offspring and attend to their needs for an unusually extended period; a complex social system based on sharing and cooperation; purposefulness, the ability to build in the brain, to scheme and plot with a vision of the outcome; communication by speech, art and writing.

Not all of these can be regarded as primary. The importance of walking bipedally is that the hands are freed to manipulate things, making the evolution of a large brain more likely and then toolmaking, art and written communication possible. Which, then, are the primary factors? Naturally different authorities have different emphases. We shall discuss them here to get some clues to indicate what characteristics an intelligent dinosaur might have.

- Bipedalism.

Don Johanson quotes Owen Lovejoy, an expert on locomotion, as stating, "from the standpoint of pure efficiency bipedalism is a preposterous way of running". Preposterous? Inefficient? Besides humans, birds find bipedalism a perfectly efficient way of running as did many dinosaurs. Some say it was crucial to the development of mankind. Dr J.Bronowski in "The Ascent of Man" writes, "when he put his foot on the ground and walked upright, man made a commitment to a new integration of life and therefore of his limbs". "The origin of bipedalism must be seen as one of the major steps, if not the major step, in human evolution", says Richard Leakey, a leading authority on the origins of mankind. He continues, "habitually walking around on the hindlimbs, leaving the forelimbs free for other jobs, is an unusual (sic) mode of locomotion. Once our ancestors had adopted an upright stance many things associated with being human became possible, such as fine manipulation with the hands, and the carrying of food back to base camp."

Yet, if bipedalism is so vital to being human and is "a new integration of life", and dinosaurs had made this commitment two hundred million years before man, why didn't they develop human characteristics? Is it possible they did? The change to bipedalism required major changes in our ancestors' anatomy; bones, muscles, internal organs all had to alter. Dinosaurs did not need such drastic modification. They had evolved as bipedal animals.

Why did our ancestors become upright? Not "so that man could make tools" as old fashioned schoolbooks told us. Evolution is not conscious – it cannot think ahead and make arrangements to meet its purposes. Furthermore, man was walking upright two million years before tools were made. The Laetoli footprints and Johanson's discoveries show that primates were walking about fully erect almost four million years ago. The crude stone tools at found at Hadar were possibly 2.5 million years old, but some prefer an age of two million years. Watching for predators is a more likely answer. Another is to do with feeding habits. Baboons partially sit upright while seeking scattered food items. Perhaps primitive prehominids did the same. Moving about upright would also have allowed food to be carried away to be eaten at leisure safe from predators. Gradually, because it conferred such advantages, they adopted the upright stance permanently. Such arguments emphasize the immense start the dinosaurs had in being upright from the beginning.

- Brain size.

Carl Sagan in "Dragons of Eden" gives four reasons, all to do with the brain, why intelligence in apes emerged only in the last few million years. (1) The brain had to grow bigger than a critical size. (2) The ratio of brain to body mass had to exceed a certain value. (3) The brain had to make more neural connections than before. (4) The brain had to evolve particular functions (in the frontal and temporal lobes perhaps). The first three imply only a quantitative change was needed but the fourth requires qualitative change instead (or as well).

It is plain from the fossil record that in the series of species that led up to man there has been a growth in brain capacity from about 350 cm^3 in the apes to a maximum of about 2000 cm^3 in recent and modern men. The human baby's brain is now so large that mothers often experience difficult and painful childbirth.

The English anatomists of Piltdown fame, Woodward and Keith, defined 750 cm^3 as the critical size for intelligence. Later Le Gros Clark reduced it to 700 cm^3. These definitions were purely arbitrary. Brain size alone is not now regarded as sufficient to define a species – it is too variable. Cranial capacity in people today ranges from 1000 cm^3 to 2000 cm^3. Earlier hominids had brain capacities that overlapped considerably with preceding and succeeding ones. The H.erectus range was 700 to 1250 cm^3, overlapping with the H.sapiens range. The H.habilis range was 500 to 800 cm^3, overlapping that of H.erectus. And Hominid brains only started to get bigger than apes' about two million years ago, apparently concurrently with the making of tools. The range is continuous and offers no basis in itself for deciding when intelligence occurred.

What is more, brain size does not correlate with intelligence, though there is a correlation between brain size and body size. Men have larger brains than women because they have larger bodies – but they are no more intelligent than women. When fossil craniums are found that appear the same save for their size, they are likely to differ only in the sex of their owner. Big brained people are not generally more intelligent than smaller brained people. Our brains seem to have overdeveloped for some reason – only a part is used. The bulk varies in size from person to person but, being unused, does not affect intelligence. A creature with a much smaller brain using it more efficiently might be capable of behavior just as sophisticated as our own.

According to David Attenborough, "the macaques are one of the most successful and versatile of all primates". Although they have a small brain compared with ours, it is complex and large for their size and they are intelligent and adaptable. Some macaques have become media personalities in the last few decades. A group of Japanese macaques living in the cold mountains of northern Japan found some volcanic springs. Quickly the whole troop learnt how to shelter in the warmth of the hot spring water. In 1953 Japanese scientists were attempting to study a troop of macaques on the small island of Koshimu. To lure them into the open for ease of observation the scientist took to burying sweet potatoes in the sand. The monkeys were troubled by the dirt on the tubers until one female in a flash of gestalt took a tuber to a rock pool and rinsed away the particles of sand. Within a few months the whole troop had spotted and picked up the trick. The same monkey also discovered how to separate rice and sand by throwing the mixture into a pool and skimming off the rice. If the thinking animal's niche were vacant, these monkeys could evolve into it over the next few million years – and they might still have the chance!

A bigger brained animal will be more intelligent than a smaller brained one, all else being equal. But since all else is not equal, we cannot be definite about a threshold brain size for intelligence.

- Brain to body ratio.

A better criterion of intelligence might be the ratio of the brain's weight to that of the whole body. This allows for the tendency of larger creatures to have larger brains simply to regulate their larger bodies. Sagan gives the ratio of body to brain weights for the Hominids as: 90 for A.robustus; 50 for A.africanus; 60 for H.habilis; 65 for H.erectus; 45 for H.sapiens. There seems to have been no significant decrease in this ratio since A.africanus and indeed the early toolmaking hominids seem to have had smaller brains for their body size than the non-toolmaking A.africanus. A.robustus, if descended from A.africanus, obviously regressed considerably – though there is some margin of error in these ratios.

More importantly, the European pygmy shrew with a body weight of 4.7 grams and a brain weight of 0.1 grams has a body to brain weight ratio of 47, very similar to our own. On this criterion pygmy shrews should be as intelligent as us! Evidently it is no criterion.

Sagan's two remaining criteria, the quantitative change in the number of neural connections leading on to the qualitative change needed for the development of different specialisms by the brain are probably more relevant. Regrettably, these are not easy to measure, though some clues can be had from casts of the interior of skulls. Bulges in certain parts of the brain can be related to the development of certain functions – like speech.

- Speech.

According to the biologist, George Gaylord Simpson, speech is "the single most diagnostic trait of mankind". David Attenborough writes: "Man's passion to communicate and to receive communications seems as central to his success as a species as the fin was to the fish or the feather to the birds."

Speech itself leaves no fossil records but we noted that the development of the lobes of the brain gives some clues. The part responsible for speech is Broca's area. All the hominids have a swollen Broca's area though it is most pronounced in man. Even in chimpanzees there is evidence of swelling here, suggesting a growth in conscious articulation. The shape of upper and lower mandibles also can give clues because of their need to accommodate the speaking mammal's unusual tongue. Speech seems to be recent. Arguably it started as long as 100,000 years ago but did not become well developed until 45,000 years ago. "Rational thinking that is purely verbal is probably only tens or hundreds of thousands of years old," Robert Bakker tells us. Were people before then not human?

No one has any real idea how or why speech evolved. People have no need to speak to make tools, to hunt or to draw pictures. Our best guess is that it develops as a form of social cement for intelligent and social creatures that have largely lost their sense of smell and are close to developing the formalized social structures that become civilization. It is a derivative of and a symptom of intelligence rather than a factor in its birth.

- Long childhood.

Is extended parental care the essential ingredient? There are two extreme strategies for propagation of the species. One requires the laying and distribution of many small eggs which the parents leave to their own devices knowing that a few will survive. Let us call this the negligent strategy. In the other a lot of parental energy and attention is devoted to the few eggs and offspring they produce. Let us call the latter the indulgent strategy.

Though the negligent approach is more common for less complicated life forms, the higher life forms are not the only caring parents. Even some fish build nests and protect their young, by hiding them in their mouths, for example. Cold-blooded turtles adopt the negligent approach. They lay large numbers of eggs on a remote beach then swim off leaving the hatchlings to fend for themselves. But cold-blooded alligators build a nest mound for their eggs, guard it, help the hatchlings to free themselves then protect them in a nursery as they grow – an indulgent strategy. Dinosaurs did not produce many eggs indicating an indulgent strategy, and were at least as attentive parents as alligators.

The higher primates have taken the indulgent strategy to its ultimate conclusion. They have only single young, very infrequently, and spend a lot of parental time and energy in raising them – chimpanzees have one child every five years only. Primate parents have a lot of responsibility and need to be resourceful – natural selection has therefore strongly favored intelligence. Perhaps this is the really crucial factor in human development?

Yet an extremely indulgent strategy is hazardous. Disease and misfortune to parents or young can be disastrous, despite any amount of parental care. When a child is dependent on its parents for a long time, the death of a parent can be the death of the child. If the child dies the parents have wasted a lot of their resources and energy and have to start the slow process again. The indulgent strategy has not been successful for the great apes. Today all apes except man have small populations in narrow geographical ranges on the verge of extinction. Why should it have succeeded for humans?

Anthropologist, Owen Lovejoy believes that bipedalism was the key to a successful modification of the indulgent strategy by mankind. By learning to walk bipedally the human female was no longer restricted to only one child at a time as were the other apes. She could gather food for herself and he older children while nurturing her baby. The change was drastic enough to trigger the evolution of a train of complementary features – continuous ovulation, pair bonding, sexual attraction between individuals, parental care, intelligence, need for larger brain at birth, need for learning, longer childhood, social grouping and toolmaking. The emergence of each trait stimulated the evolution of others in a complicated evolutionary pattern.

But in the sense that parental nurturing and care is longer and more intensive in humans than in any other primates, humans adopt the ultimately indulgent strategy. The other primates were not successful but mankind is. Lovejoy's explanation is that the human strategy is less indulgent than the apes'. But, if being able to cope with more than one demanding child at a time makes the strategy less extreme than in other primates, it has surely only become true since human beings took to gardening 10,000 years ago. The hunter gatherers remaining today, like the T'Kung of South West Africa, have a reproductive strategy similar to that of the savannah apes.

Hunter-gatherer women do not ovulate while the previous child is still suckling and cannot become pregnant while suckling a child. But T'Kung women suckle their children until they are four years' old by which time the child, though still dependent on parental support, is able to begin to help with the gathering. Thus the natural interval between successive children in human hunter gatherer females does not differ greatly from the chimpanzee's. But the care invested in each offspring by humans is much higher because it takes much longer for a human baby to become independent. Human precursors had a more extremely indulgent strategy than the other great apes not a lesser one. Furthermore some of the other characteristics of intelligence seem to depend heavily on a highly indulgent strategy. Purposefulness, creativity and imagination; thinking ahead, anticipating and predicting are all qualities which may be partly innate but need stimulation and teaching to develop. Attentive parents and a close social organization are necessary for this. For humans, if the degree of indulgence has fallen at all, it has only been since agriculture was invented.

Having left the Garden of Eden human females stopped suckling earlier and lost the natural contraceptive protection that went with it. A natural restriction on the growth of population had been removed. "Civilized" women do not suckle their children at all. They feed their children on the milk of domestic animals. The result is that they begin to ovulate immediately and can be pregnant again within 12 months. After the loss of natural contraception and before artificial contraception was introduced, human females probably had three or four times as many children as they would have had naturally. So it is hardly surprising then that population should have exploded in the last 10,000 years.

- Cooperation.

Cooperation developed from the longer dependency of human young on their mother. A division of labor occurred. The females, responsible for bringing up the children, undertook the placid activity of gathering, providing a degree of security and the group's reliable food supplies. The males, with less responsibility and able to risk their security, sought to get the richer animal protein, initially through scavenging for animal remains and later by actively hunting. But it was not how the food was obtained that triggered the emergence of mankind but the joint manner in which food was eaten and the cementing of social bonds that it entailed. While gathering, the females shared her food and her experience with her children, male and female. Males, used to sharing with their mothers, brothers and sisters, gradually adopted it as adults realizing that sharing provided more secure returns than individual prospecting. The sharing culture spread and eventually societies became more cooperative rather than purely competitive.

Baboons do not share although they do forage together. Chimps rarely share and when they do it is normally after prolonged scrounging. The habit acquired by human males from their mothers, of sharing food, distinguished humans from other primates where the dominant male was more likely to steal it, and led to cooperation and economic interdependence. Hunting and tool making were luxuries that could be enjoyed because the females provided a secure base for the human group through food gathering. Even the first tools – sticks for reaching and digging, stones for cracking nuts, sharp stones for cutting roots, and bark for containers – might have been made by women to assist gathering. The technological invention that led to mankind might not have been the hand axe used by the hunters but rather the container which allowed a lot of food items to be collected by the gatherers, the women and children, and transported back to base for communal eating later.

- Hunting.

Several million years ago several environmental niches were filled by clever and adventurous primates. Chimpanzees, being woodland animals, mainly ate fruit. Baboons, like men, had moved on to the savannah and lived on roots, grass and seeds (both baboons and chimpanzees ate meat but it constituted only five per cent of their diet). The savannah apes had a similar territory and diet to the baboons but had discovered new strategies. The division of labor and sharing freed their males to spend more time getting meat. Gathering would continue to give the communes of apes reliable basic sustenance, but scavenging and then hunting provided concentrated protein. This was a vital step forward giving the apes time to think, and later time to philosophize. Herbivorous elephants have to spend three quarters of their time eating their low quality food. The carnivorous lion on the other hand only spends about 15 per cent of its time seeking and eating its food rich in protein.

The step to scavenging was fairly easy. There was always some recently dead creature not far away on the savannah and the alert apes would have noticed circling vultures. At Sterkfontein in South Africa, Elisabeth Vrba and Philip Tobias found accumulations of savannah ape bones apparently collected by a predator (possibly a leopard) in its den. There were no stone tools in that layer but in a higher and more recent layer there were stone tools and a pattern of animal remains typical of a scavenger. It seems that the scavenger (Homo habilis) was a toolmaker while his predecessor who made no tools (A.africanus) was prey. From scavenging it was not such a large step for the emergent men to appreciate that carcasses could be created.

Sherwood Washburn in 1956 argued that hunting was the key to human development. Washburn reasoned that, because the apes were slow they had to substitute cunning and cooperation for speed. The new art of hunting in groups required an effective means of communication at a distance: the development of language was the result. The hunting theory of Washburn became accentuated into the theory of "the killer ape" promoted by Robert Ardrey. Robert Ardrey says, "Man is man and not a chimpanzee, because for millions upon millions of years we killed for a living". But killing for a living cannot have led to speech. Shouting to companions is the last thing that a hunter would do if he did not want his prey to bolt, and speaking arose too late to have been triggered by hunting millions of years before.

The contentment of the hunter-gatherers and their sensitivity to their environment belies the hunting hypothesis of human aggressiveness. The hunter-gatherer way of life is not one of grinding insecurity, incessant toil and hardship. It offers as much, if not more, leisure than people have today. Hunter gatherer communities have total confidence in their ability to obtain sustenance from their environment and feel no need to store or save for the long term. Though it no longer appeals to us, pampered by our advanced technology, hunter-gathering is comfortable and secure to those brought up to it. Moreover, many of today's hunter-gatherers like the San of South West Africa have been forced by gardeners and farmers into harsh environments on the margins of deserts. They comfortably survive, but, before they were thrust to the desert margins, the hunter-gatherers would have had much lusher pickings. It is no exaggeration to call it the "Garden of Eden" – all was provided simply by reaching out or digging up a root. Marshall Sahlins who has studied stone age economics in depth assures us "all people's wants are easily satisfied". Males of the T'Kung hunt for only 21 hours a week and the women (who provide two thirds of the food) gather for only 12 hours. In terrain which to us is inhospitable desert, they have sufficient.

Richard Leakey thinks our aggression may be a pathological response to the human condition that has emerged since the first urban communities of 10,000 years ago. He writes, "for perhaps two million years, human ancestors had practised nomadic hunting-and-gathering, in a way of life that was characterized by stability rather than change in terms of technology and culture. Then the ancient way of life was virtually abandoned over a period of a few thousand years." We may be still suffering the trauma of that immense change.

But mankind hunted animals to extinction long before we were shown the gate of the Garden of Eden. Of the savannah apes, the steps to scavenging and hunting were too great for A.robustus. They did not realize the value of meat or, if they did, they found competition with Homo and the baboons too difficult. Homo forced them to eat less nutritious food needing a lot of processing. They evolved jaws suitable for low grade food but were marginalized by their proto-human rivals, became their prey and were pushed into extinction. Were our insensitivity to the other inhabitants of the Garden, our incompetence as custodians and our genocidal destructiveness the reasons for our expulsion? Have present day hunter-gatherers been marginalized precisely because they are not aggressive enough? A killer instinct is possibly a contributory factor to world domination, generating a particularly aggressive competitiveness that has been partly instrumental in mankind's progress. Of course, many dinosaurs were savage killers too – our killer instinct might be part of our dinosaur heritage.

This survey suggests some factors that influenced the emergence of the intelligent mammal. They are: manipulative forelimbs with grasping fingers and opposable thumbs; binocular vision; color vision; omnivorous diet; curiosity and opportunism; upright posture; exceptionally lengthy childhood dependence on parental care enabling teaching to occur with development of higher skills and creativity; large brain; toolmaking; sharing, division of labor and cooperation; aggression and a callous indifference to other species, as well as other humans, fostered by hunting.

Have the dinosaurs of 70 million years ago left any signs of their having any of these characteristics? I shall explore this in the next chapter.

CHAPTER FIVE

...BUT A THINKING DINOSAUR?

"It is tempting to hope that the most original achievements of the mind are also the most recent."

J.Bronowski

Dr Brian Stableford is a biology graduate and lecturer in sociology at the University of Reading, England, but is better known as a writer of science fiction. He writes in "The Science in Science Fiction" that "...certain difficulties stand in the way of the ever popular lizard-men who figure so frequently as science fictional villains. Reptiles, having no internal temperature control, are rather limited in the amount of brain activity they can indulge in..." That may be true of lizard-men but not of dinosaur-men or dinosauroids, to use the word coined by Dale Russell of the National Museum of Natural Sciences in Ottawa, Canada. Dinosauroids are intelligent creatures evolved from dinosaurs, and because dinosaurs had a physiology superior to lizards and in many ways superior to mammals, Dr Stableford's complaint does not hold water. Our anthroposaur and Russell's dinosauroid are Dr Stableford's lizard-men precisely because they are all lizard-men could be. Anthroposaur is the better term: it is more descriptive than Russell's word, and Russell's conception of dinosaur evolution was vastly different from that considered here. Russell imagined how dinosaurs might have evolved had they survived the Cretaceous-Tertiary (K-T) extinction and remained alive until today. They didn't survive, so they couldn't evolve. But the anthroposaurs could have evolved before the K-T catastrophe, as we shall see.

Stableford informally lists the characteristics of an intelligent organism. "If human beings did not walk upright, freeing their forelimbs to develop hands instead of paws, they could not have developed the kind of intelligence they have. Similarly intelligent beings must be sociable, because intelligence arises out of the need to communicate. The fact that most mammals and birds show a degree of intelligence not seen in reptiles is connected with the fact that they generally have more complicated social relationships, especially in connection with the rearing of young. The more sociable animals are, and the more able they are to interfere with and transform their environment, the more intelligent they become."

Stableford's characteristics tally respectably with those deduced from our study of mankind's emergence. The ones which we have some chance of assessing rationally 65 million years after the death of the dinosaurs other than warm-bloodedness, are: intelligent terrestrial animals are bipedal, have an erect stance; are equipped with grasping hands having sensitive fingers and opposable thumbs; are equipped with binocular vision; own a large brain; are subject to social and parental guidance in childhood; are able to speak; are aggressive. How do the dinosaurs measure up?

- Bipedal.

From what Bakker and Ostrom discovered during the 1970s, dinosaurs offer remarkable possibilities for the development of intelligence. We have seen that dinosaurs fulfilled the requirement of bipedalism early on – the reason for their supremacy was their upright, bipedal stance. Bipedalism gave dinosaurs a head start on mammals in the race for intelligence because it was the very basis of their evolutionary emergence. Like the hominids, having discovered that they could run on their hind legs, they must eventually have realized that their forelimbs were freed for the manipulation of objects.

- Manipulative hands.

What, then, of grasping hands? To be of maximum use this means that one of the digits, the thumb, should be opposed enabling its tip to touch the tip of the other digits. Is there evidence that the dinosaurs were able to grasp things? The answer is that opposed digits were very common in dinosaurs. Even the Tyrannosaurids and other large carnivores had an opposed toe rather like perching birds, but T.rex's forelimbs, we noted, had degenerated into crutches to help it get out of bed. The feathered dinosaur, the archaeopteryx, certainly had grasping hands, as did its near relatives the coelurosaurs, and surely used them for grasping insects and climbing trees.

A related but later dinosaur that seemed to have evolved a high degree of coordination of hands and arms was the deinonychus. Its "hands [were] better adapted for grasping and holding than any other dinosaur" (Desmond). Deinonychus had long, grasping hands with wrist joints that rotated so that the hands could turn towards each other enabling the animal to grasp its prey in both hands. Wilford's comment is that "only humans and certain other mammals can do this".

The Late Cretaceous, the period we are chiefly interested in, was full of examples. Some descendants of deinonychus formed a whole group called the dromaeosaurs all of which had opposable fingers and were obviously capable of a high degree of coordination. One of the descendants of deinonychus was a dinosaur discovered by Dale Russell called the stenonychosaurus. This animal had manipulating fingers, but also had a complex of advanced features, including binocular vision, that make it rather special. Plainly some dinosaurs combined a bipedal gait with sensitive, manipulative hands.

- Binocular vision.

Binocular vision is, you will recall, the ability to direct both eyes simultaneously at an object. In considering the evolution of man it was coupled with manipulating hands in early primates and is considered basic to the development of intelligence. The importance of this ability for the growth of the brain is that it allows a better judgment of distance, valuable for leaping and throwing. It stimulates three dimensional thinking. The evolution of manufacturing levels of intelligence requires the development of hand and eye coordination. Without the ability to see stereoscopically, it seems unlikely that it would be possible to think stereoscopically and thereby to erect structures in the mind prior to building them on the ground.

Many creatures alive today besides man have binocular vision, birds of prey like the owl, for instance, but they do not often combine it with grasping hands. Binocular vision in tyrannosaurus was facilitated by the snout being very narrow so as not to impair its line of sight. But tyrannosaurus, as we have seen, had atrophied arms and the real evolutionary advantage comes when the binocular vision is combined with skillful hands.

The stenonychosaurus had binocular vision combined with manipulative hands and fingers. Its eyes were large and well developed like the eyes of the ostrich (which has the largest eyes of any terrestrial creature alive today). This in itself is an interesting feature because it suggests that these dinosaurs were nocturnal or that they had evolved not long before from a nocturnal form. Two points from this. First, it is further evidence, should anyone need convincing, that the dinosaurs were warm-blooded, because cold-blooded animals must be inactive at night. Second, what would they be hunting at night time that needed speed, agility, keen vision and grasping hands? None other than our predecessors, the mammals. "It was not until the Cretaceous that we find signs that the mammals were hounded even into the night. They were terrorized, moreover, by creatures more cunning than themselves", as Desmond puts it. Yes, the mammals were small, but these dinosaurs were also small by dinosaur standards – stenonychosaurus was only about five feet long including its long tail. Here then is a dinosaur with keen senses, nimble and agile enough to hunt, by night, the supposedly superior mammals!

- Brains.

Let us turn now to the size of the dinosaurian brain. Carl Sagan writes, "the entire evolutionary record on our planet, particularly the record contained in fossil endocasts, illustrates a progressive tendency toward intelligence." This is Marsh's Law: brains grow from generation to generation. But it is not true of cold-blooded animals. Whereas a modern cat of the same body size as a sabre-toothed tiger of 30 million years ago has twice the brain volume, a modern crocodile has just the same volume of brain matter as an ancestor of comparable size 200 million years ago. The brains of even advanced cold-bloods like crocodiles violate Marsh's law.

But Marsh formulated his law from studying dinosaur brains!

The popular idea that the dinosaurs were dim witted, with brains no bigger than a ping-pong ball is only partly true. It appertains to the huge sauropods, ceratopsians and some carnosaurs – the dinosaurs well known to the layman. A triceratops' body weighed 9000 times more than its brain, a hadrosaur's body weighed 20,000 times more, and a brontosaurus's weighed 100,000 times more. But it is not true of many others dinosaurs, the ones noted above with the grasping hands and binocular vision, the smaller, agile coelurosaurs and dromaeosaurs that lived late into the Cretaceous period. Knowing what we do about these, it is not so surprising that they had evolved large brains to coordinate their sophisticated movements and vision.

Deinonychus had the odd but effective habit of standing on one leg while slashing its victim with a vicious talon on the other. Such balancing tricks, even accepting that the creature would have its prey firmly in its grip, required remarkable brain development. The descendants of deinonychus, the family of dromaeosaurs, were agile, skilful predators with large brains. Few good fossils have been found but it has been conjectured that they were more common, and more successful, than the fossil record suggests, their habitats not being conducive to fossilization – just like the apes and hominids, mankind's ancestors!

The body to brain ratio of the stenonychosaurus was 1000. This doesn't signal much intelligence compared with a human being whose ratio is about 50, but it is comparable to a living flightless bird like the emu. It is also within a factor of about six of the ratio for a chimpanzee. Yet a bird-mimic dinosaur, the dromiceiomimus, had a brain bigger than an ostrich's. Birds, despite the derogatory expression "bird brain", are remarkably intelligent. They are caring parents and often have a hierarchical social system epitomized by their "pecking order". Large brained flightless birds such as the ostrich live together in flocks and also had some social organization suggesting that the dromiceiomimus did likewise.

Pterosaurs were flying dinosaurs. In modern day birds the ability to fly has required substantial development of their brains, particularly in the cerebellum region at the back of the brain and the cerebral region at the front of the brain. The cerebellum controls movement and balance while the cerebral region looks after coordination, both plainly important to a flying creature. The fascinating aspect of the pterosaurs was that their brains had developed exactly these features by convergent evolution. Like birds their olfactory sense had atrophied and instead they had well developed optic lobes. The optic lobes had been pushed by the growth of the cerebellum and cerebral regions to the sides and rear of the brain. Exactly the same had occurred in birds!

Even more similarities between the physiology of pterosaurs and birds could be listed but they are not relevant here. Suffice it to say that some pterosaurs were as small as a sparrow and that would be impossible for a cold-blooded or a naked warm-blooded creature. A cold-blooded vertebrate could hardly have generated the energy needed to fly. External insulation was needed for a warm-blood to maintain its high internal temperature. Pterosaur fossils have been found with clear impressions of fur on them. They must have looked like a cross between a fledgling bird and a bat, and they succeeded in holding their own against the birds for 90 million years until the cataclysm that marked the end of the Cretaceous era. But despite their obvious intelligence and fur coats, bat-like dinosaurs were not principle contenders for the honor of developing any sort of technology.

- Parental care.

Dale Russell, in a paper in the Canadian Journal Of Earth Sciences in 1972, discussing the bird-mimic, dromiceiomimus, suggested that parental care seemed likely in animals with such intelligence and with evidence of a social organization. But even Sagan writing in 1977 thought it "unlikely that [the dinosaurs] actively protected either eggs or young". Typical reptiles!

Nile crocodiles are reptilian enough but, we've already seen, are caring parents, having quite a sophisticated social and family life: the male is territorial; he courts the female; she builds a nest; she lays about 40 eggs; when the young are ready to hatch they warn mom from the egg using piping sounds audible several yards away; mom carefully digs them out and carries them tenderly in batches in her jaws to a nursery near the river or swamp; while the young learn how to live by hunting frogs and fish, the parents dutifully keep watch over them; after several months they are able to fend for themselves. If cold-blooded crocs are as doting as this why shouldn't warm-blooded dinosaurs have been?

Exhibit 4. Some possibilities for the precursors of the intelligent dinosaurs.

- The coelurosaurs were small, lightly built fast running predators. They had small heads with sharp teeth, moderately long necks and long arms with grasping hands. Animals of this type must have been abundant during the 140 million years reign of the dinosaurs but because of their slightly built physiology they decayed and their bones were scavenged quickly so that few specimens have been found. The dromaeosaurids, which seemed to have evolved from coelurosaurs, lived at the end of the Cretaceous.
- Compsognathus was a small (two feet long) dinosaur about the weight of a hen from the end of the Jurassic, 140 million years ago. It was clearly fast and could catch nimble creatures as its prey. Its hand only had two digits and its forelimbs were short, putting its grasping abilities in doubt, but in the time period up to the end of the Cretaceous its descendants could have well adapted along the required lines.
- Ornitholestes lived about the same time as compsognathus but was bigger and had a more powerful head. Its arms were long and it had three digits two of which were long and the other, the thumb, short but opposed. It would have been quite good at grasping and could have diversified into even better forms.
- The ornithomimosaurs had three digit hands, long arms, large brains and opposed thumbs. Oviraptorosaurs which fall into the same category had grasping hands. Saurornithoidids like stenonychosaurus could have hunted the mammals into the night and sharpened their intelligence against that of our distant ancestors. These dinosaurs were thought by Dale Russell capable of evolving intelligence.

More familiar are birds, which lay eggs and devote an astonishing amount of parental care to them. Bakker tells us that birds are living dinosaurs. If so, dinosaurs must have been just as attentive to their eggs and as indulgent to their hatchlings.

Dinosaur eggs are quite rare. None were found until in midsummer 1923, Roy Chapman Andrews and his team exploring the Gobi desert found nests of dinosaur eggs, some of which contained the fossil embryos of a dinosaur, protoceratops, a precursor of the giant ceratopsians of the Late Cretaceous. Yet eggs have a hard exterior and would be expected to be easily fossilized. When the dinosaur's ancestors emerged from the swamps, one of the advantages they had over their competitors, the amphibians, was the hard exterior of their eggs. Amphibians laid soft eggs like those of modern frogs and newts. These would be unsuitable for an animal that had ambitions of living on dry land. Amphibians had to have water nearby – not so, the dinosaurs. Their hard eggs enclosed a watery fluid in a sac called the amnion. Within this the embryo developed, feeding on its self-contained food supply in the yolk. Foetuses of mammals including humans are similarly enclosed in a sac of amniotic fluid which bursts shortly before birth.

In summer 1978 in Montana, two fossil hunters found a nest of fifteen fossilized baby dinosaurs each about three feet long. They were not hatchlings because their teeth were worn showing that they had been eating for some time. Further work exposed a whole treasure trove of dinosaurs' nests, a veritable hadrosaurs' roost of 300 eggs and over 60 skeletons of dinosaurs of all ages from embryos to adults. The nests, which were about six or seven feet across, were about 20 feet apart leaving sufficient room for the bulky parents to gain access.

Some of the nests contained only broken shells, the nestlings presumably having left the nest, but some contained immature skeletons of varying sizes, presumably because the nest had been abandoned for some reason and the young hadrosaurs had starved to death. The physiology of the skeletons confirmed that dinosaur babies grew rapidly from a very small size. The eggs were oval shaped with a maximum dimension of about eight inches, providing enough room for hatchlings only about 15 to 20 inches long. Such small, vulnerable animals, growing rapidly, must have been warm-blooded. The remains often included eight feet long juveniles alongside 20 feet long adults suggesting that parents and young stayed together until the young were mature. The ratio of juveniles to adults seems to have been about two to one. The following year nests of another dinosaur, the hypsilophodont, were found containing up to two dozen eggs, and about fifteen skeletons of juveniles were found nearby. As John Noble Wilford puts it, "dinosaurs ... had a sense of family life and community."

Why had baby dinosaurs not been found before? They had! But the experts had classified them as new species of small dinosaurs rather than seeing them as juveniles of species already identified. Furthermore, mental fix had led dinosaur hunters into looking in particular types of strata to make their finds. These were rocks laid down on lowland plains or in shallow bays or estuaries. The Montana dinosaur colonies were on dryer rockier outcrops where the nests were perhaps safer from predators.

Must all dinosaurs have laid eggs? Not even all modern reptiles lay eggs. Snakes, skinks, some amphibians (salamanders) and even some fish (sharks, guppies and sea horses) keep their eggs within themselves until birth.

- The sea snakes of the Indian Ocean give birth to live young (viviparity). They do not have a placenta like the mammals to nourish the embryo while it is developing, but nevertheless they do keep their eggs within their bodies until they are hatched.
- Rattlesnakes are even more advanced. They retain their eggs and have even dispensed with a hard shell. The embryo not only gets

nutriment from a yolk but also by diffusion of sustenance from the mother across the thin outer membrane of the egg, a support system very suggestive of a placenta. At birth the mother continues to look after the young.

- One species of frog, gastrotheca, keeps its young in a pouch until they hatch into tadpoles when they are released into the water, but another species keeps them in its pouch until they emerge as baby frogs.

- A West African toad, nectophrynoides, retains its eggs in its oviduct. When the tadpoles hatch they feed upon particles released from the walls of the oviduct and at the next wet season live baby toads are born, the mother having provided a pseudo pond for them within her oviduct.

- Amazingly, the coelacanth, a fish thought to have been extinct for 70 million years until found again in 1938, gives birth to live young. This creature is believed not to have evolved in any significant way for hundreds of millions of years indicating that creatures had live offspring before the dinosaurs even appeared on earth.

Following a discovery made by an assistant in 1947 in New Mexico, Edwin Holbert found several fossilized skeletons of a small early dinosaur called coelophysis. Coelophysis was an early type of coelurosaurus living at the end of the Triassic period about 210 million years ago. A remarkable graveyard of these specimens was found in New Mexico. Bones were weathering out of a rock stratum in a hillside and some had been recovered by a collector as long ago as 1881. Thus the species had been known for 60 years but previous specimens had been poor: these were excellent. When the site was rediscovered it was agreed to dig away the overlying strata and look at the layer containing the fossils. An amazing lode of coelophysis bones was found, young and old together. The amazing feature of one of them, Colbert noted, was that it seemed to have inside it the bones of a tiny juvenile. Colbert could not accept the obvious inference that the dinosaur gave birth to live young, especially as the pelvic bones seemed too narrow. He deduced that the "baby" was actually the adult's last meal.

Live birth did occur in ichthyosaurs, the dolphin-like dinosaurs. At first, paleontologists, faced with the idea of sea-dinosaurs, thought they must leave the sea to lay their eggs like turtles. But the ichthyosaurs were far too whale-like for that to happen. An ichthyosaur would be no more able to crawl up a beach than a porpoise or a killer whale – on land it would be literally stranded. It also seemed odd that no ichthyosaur eggs could ever be found. Even though masses of ichthyosaur fossils were found at Holzmaden in Germany there were no signs of any eggs. And this despite the discovery of fossilized ichthyosaur droppings (called coproliths) that would plainly have been less suitable for fossilization than eggs.

The answer came from our friend, the noted amateur, Bernard Hauff, who owned those productive quarries in Holzmaden and made a name for himself by the skill he put into the delicate process of extracting the imprint from the rock matrix. He conclusively showed that some of the ichthyosaurs had smaller specimens inside them. As we might expect, this triggered off a controversy about the "baby" ichthyosaurs. "They are not unborn babies but part of the larger creature's last dinner," was the cry. It is far from unknown for vertebrates, especially fish, to eat their own young. The small specimens inside the body of the larger specimen were always facing forwards, in the direction of motion of the larger fossil. "If the animal were to be born it would have its head to the rear – animals are always born head first," pronounced the critics. "What's more, a swimming creature being pursued and finally swallowed by another would be swallowed tail first and would be bound to be 'head forward' in the predator's stomach."

Hauff countered by showing what the larger ichthyosaurs had had for dinner – mainly a variety of types of swimming shelled molluscs having a lifestyle similar to modern squids. The experts remained unmoved. Hauff responded by providing the ultimate proof. He had had a slab of rock needing cleaning for a long time but had constantly sidelined it as more promising finds were brought to him. When he did remove the extraneous rock, he was amazed to find that the impression was one of an ichthyosaur in the act of giving birth. The smaller specimen was hanging below the body of the parent yet with its foreparts still evidently within the mother's body.

It is now known that whales give birth in this fashion, tail first, to allow the tail of the foetus to get strong in the stream of water flowing over the mother's body. The infant whale will dangle thus for four to six weeks, the birth only being completed when the baby is strong enough to swim alongside its mother. Once again the similarity of function in similar environments and lifestyles demonstrates itself. Efficient evolution into a particular ecological niche generates the same solution to problems of adaptation. We shall have reason to remember this when the question of the evolution of intelligence is considered in more detail.

The sauropods like brontosaurus also could have given birth to live young. Tracks of sauropods indicate that they moved about in groups, if not herds. Bakker has found that dinosaur herds were structured such that the young were protected in the middle by a surrounding circle of adults, showing that the young were evidently cared for after birth, viviparous or otherwise. Yet, if they laid eggs, there are several problems to answer. Did the herd stop in one locality while the eggs hatched? If they did, would not such dim-witted animals trample all over the eggs before they had time to hatch. If not, how did the young rejoin the herd, which had presumably moved on after the egg laying? Furthermore, eggs cannot be larger than a certain maximum size since beyond that size they would either collapse under their own weight or they would have to be so tough that the hatchling would not be able to crack the shell to emerge. The maximum size is small for such huge dinosaurs as brontosaurus and its relatives, which reached 50 tons or more at maturity. Even if the eggs were three feet across like those of the extinct bird, the aepyornis, the hatchlings would be still likely to be crushed underfoot.

All these problems are answered if the young were carried until they had reached a reasonable level of maturity. At birth they would then have been able to keep up with the wanderings of the herd and avoid the clumsy feet of their elders. They would also have been big enough not to lose heat to their surroundings. Bakker believes the sauropods' live young weighed as much as 500 pounds at birth, solving most problems, but if they were smaller the problems remained. Could sauropods have carried their young in pouches rather like a kangaroo? The problem then is what they could have fed on. Kangaroos are mammals with teats to provide nourishing milk. One assumes that we are on safe ground in believing that not even hot blooded dinosaurs had mammalia! Could the young have snuggled into a pouch near to the sauropod's tail feeding upon the parent's dung. Since they were too small to avoid rapid heat loss, they would also be kept warm by their mother's body heat. The large herbivorous dinosaurs probably had to allow their food to ferment in their stomachs because the cycads and ferns they ate were tough and fibrous. Their droppings would therefore be effectively predigested food for the infants. Many smaller creatures live on the dung of larger ones and some, like rabbits and mole rats, eat their own to make sure no nutrition is wasted.

Perhaps some of the many dinosaurs that undoubtedly did lay eggs also carried their young like marsupials, particularly to keep them from dying of heat loss when they were tiny. The upright posture of many dinosaurs is reminiscent of the posture of the kangaroo and wallaby. Though marsupials do not necessarily adopt this erect stance, it might be convenient for erect animals to adopt a marsupial method of protecting their young. Admittedly there has been no quoted instances of this, but the dinosaurs were still vigorously adapting even shortly before their final demise. Is it possible that they anticipated other vertebrate systems for protecting their young, millions of years ago? The marsupial system? The human system?

What of the pterosaurs of the Cretaceous period? Bakker scorns the experts, authors of the "most commonly used twentieth-century paleontology textbook." They concluded that the pterosaurs were "failures in everything they did." For these experts the pterosaur could not fly and could not walk. Its wings were too floppy and tore too easily. On the ground it was clumsy and ungainly. It is amazing that the poor creatures survived at all, let alone that they existed in large numbers in the Jurassic and Cretaceous periods.

In reality their success was obvious to those who correctly read the fossil evidence. They were superbly adapted to their aerial home, as earlier and wiser men like Baron Cuvier and Professor Seeley (who wrote the seminal work, "Dragons of the Air" in 1901) knew. Excellent fossils found in the 1970s showed that the wing was supported by cartilaginous membranes tensioned by strong muscles along their arms, and not by the extended fourth digit alone. There was continuous control over the whole of the surface of the wings. Pterodactyls also had powerful muscles in their breasts like birds, indicated by their deep breast bone. In all respects the pterosaur's whole anatomy can be shown to be dedicated to its commitment to powered flight.

But did they, like birds, look after their young? The pelvis of the female pterosaurs was too narrow to permit live births unless the foetus was born in an immature state. If so its tiny size would have necessitated parental care especially since it would have difficulty keeping warm despite its fur coat. More likely, eggs were laid. A family structure like that of birds would then have been needed, to hatch the eggs, to feed the immature young and to guide them in taking to the wing.

Whether dinosaurs of all types laid eggs or gave birth to live young it is certain that they were often caring parents.

- Sounds and speech.

Let us come to the important question of vocal communication. Could the dinosaurs communicate by sounds?

All dinosaurs had sensitive middle ear bones and a notch in their skull where the tight ear drum stretched. Crocodiles and birds, both of which are related to the dinosaurs, have keen hearing so it is not surprising that dinosaurs also had acute hearing. Would they then make sounds? Birds do. And present day crocodiles can recognize each other by night by making a barking noise. There seems no reason to doubt that dinosaurs, known to have acute hearing, would also have done this. But they had nothing akin to a larynx to enable them to make the sort of speech we do. Why should they? The cetaceans, our whales and porpoises, have sophisticated communication systems based on a host of sounds not made in the human way. Many of the hadrosaurs had distinctive crests protecting their elaborately long nasal passages. Philip Currie of Alberta's Tyrrell Museum suggests that these could have acted as a resonant chamber allowing the hadrosaurs to make sounds rather like a French horn.

It is surmised that Charles Sternberg's edmontosaurus had an inflatable sac on its snout that acted as a resonator enabling calls and signals to be made to other members of the herd to attract them or warn them. Elephant seals have a similar sort of arrangement. The nesting maiasaur of Montana could have made a deep base like sound by blowing air through its nasal passages.

- Hunting.

Meat, being concentrated protein, we saw, is an important factor in the development of intelligence. The animal needs less bulky food and needs less time eating. So, it has more thinking time, time free to become cultural and inventive.

Tracks of up to six carnivorous dinosaurs all moving in parallel suggests that some of them hunted in packs. If, as Washburn suggested in man, sophisticated communication and language originated to coordinate group hunting activities, intelligent dinosaurs should be looked for among those types that hunted together. Carnivores also had the other attributes of intelligence discussed in this chapter. The hadrosaurs which could surely make conspicuous noises were not carnivores but, if herbivores could make sounds, hunting dinosaurs could also have developed a sophisticated range of whistling sounds for communication – like birdsong, perhaps. Washburn's hunting hypothesis is, of course, far from convincing but, if it *were* correct, it could apply equally to dinosaurs as to mankind. Plainly, the predatory dinosaurs were aggressive enough, if that were an important attribute for technological success.

The skulls of the dinosaurs show that many had very well developed senses. The structure of their ears, indicates excellent hearing and the ability to hear high pitched noises, possibly initially the calls of their young and later the sounds of communication. Brain casts show highly developed olfactory bulbs showing the sense of smell was often good. Large orbits and pronounced optic lobes tell of excellent vision. Some were caring parents possibly having live young, had stereoscopic vision and manipulating hands. Many walked upright and some later dinosaurs had large and growing brains. Some also were fierce hunters and presumably correspondingly aggressive.

Some dinosaurs somewhere had each of the attributes considered necessary for man to evolve. The only conclusion is that some dinosaur somewhere could have had them all and become intelligent before Adam. But how? Could the same feature have evolved twice in vastly different types of animal? Certainly. Features have evolved repeatedly. We have already met several instances, ichthyosaurs and dolphins, for example. The mechanism is convergent evolution.

CHAPTER SIX

CONVERGING ON A SOLUTION

"Heaven held his hand, the likeness must be true."

W.Cowper

The Church justified its resistance to the idea of evolution in the 18th and 19th Centuries by quoting Ecclesiastes 3:14: "I know that everything God does will last for ever." Had it chosen verse 3:15 instead it would have supported Cuvier and anticipated this book: "Whatever happens or can happen has already happened before. God makes the same thing happen again and again." (Quotations from the Good News Bible.)

What is the evidence that God has made the same thing happen again and again. In evolution it is the way different species have evolved along paths that lead them to essentially the same outcome. But surely there is a law that evolution is always progressive, onwards and divergent, not regressive, backwards or convergent – Dollo's law says evolution is irreversible. But many people take it too literally. Except in a very strict sense, it is not true. A fish, hundreds of millions of years ago, left the water ultimately to evolve into terrestrial vertebrates, but land vertebrates have often taken to the water since, and have assumed the shape and lifestyles of fish. The strict sense is that they have not become fish again.

Dollo's rule can be thought of in terms of a motion picture of someone walking up a street. The man could perfectly well turn round at the top of the street and begin to walk down again and there would be nothing unusual in that. If, however, he got to the end of the street only to retrace his steps precisely but walking stiffly backwards, finishing exactly where he started and in the same posture, then we should consider it unusual. We might suspect that the motion picture had been played backward rather than that it had accurately portrayed a real event.

Dollo's rule is saying the same thing about evolution. It is vanishingly unlikely that any evolutionary path could be traced twice in either direction. But it is far from impossible, indeed it is very likely, that different organisms subject to the same evolutionary constraints will evolve marked similarities. An orange jelly made in the same mould as a strawberry blancmange will have the same shape because it has been subject to the same constraints of shape. But it remains a jelly and not a blancmange. The dolphin is not a fish but it looks very like a fish because it has been subject to the evolutionary constraints imposed by the dense aqueous medium that determined the shape of fish. This is convergent evolution. Richard Dawkins explains that if a design principle is good enough to be used once in evolution it is good enough to be used twice – though not in exactly the same way.

Convergent evolution explains the way similar features are found in different creatures though no ancestor had those common features. Parallel evolution describes the case when both species or genera have a common ancestry but where both have independently evolved common solutions in response to the same or similar evolutionary problems. Evolutionary convergence is the more extreme in the sense that the two species or genera have no immediate common ancestor. In other words, they diverged long before either type of creature evolved and yet converged towards a common set of features in response to the same environmental constraints.

Examples are powered flight which has evolved separately several times in insects, pterosaurs, birds and bats; the camera eye of vertebrates and the cephalopods; echolocation in bats, birds and whales; use of electricity in some fish; convergence in placental and marsupial mammals; and even convergence in self-replicating molecules grown in test tubes. Generally speaking uncomplicated features evolve repeatedly, but more complicated ones less often. Intelligence is such a feature.

People find it incredible that the camera eye evolved once let alone twice in the cephalopods and the vertebrates . Octopus eyes are amazingly similar in construction to the eyes of vertebrates yet have evolved quite separately. An octopus's eyes arose from skin cells, a vertebrate's from brain cells. In one respect octopus eyes are superior. The nerves taking the signals from the photoreceptors in the eye to the brain are placed behind the receptors so they do not interfere with the incoming light. In the vertebrate eye the nerves are in front of the photoreceptors interfering with the incoming light's path. The differences are fundamental and confirm that the two forms could not possibly have come from any common ancestor.

Echolocation has evolved several times, in two types of bat, two types of bird, in cetaceans, in seals and, to lesser extents in rats, shrews and humans. (Dawkins asserts that echolocation, used unconsciously, explains how some blind people can "see" with their cheeks. They are hearing subtle changes in sounds allowing them to sense obstacles in their paths.)

It is well known that bats and cetaceans use echo sounding but not so well known that birds do. Two types of birds have the ability and yet must have evolved it independently (they are unrelated and live half a world apart) – the cave swifts of the Orient and the oil birds of South America. Echolocation has evolved in both these types of bird because they nest in deep, dark caves. Their echolocation system is, however, relatively crude being based on audible sounds rather than ultrasound as used by our native bats.

Bats have quite amazingly sophisticated sonar systems. They make very loud noises, although we cannot hear them because our ears are not sensitive to the ultrasound they use, and they have large and highly sensitive ears to enable them to receive the very weak echoes that they get from the small insects they seek as food. This combination of loud noises and sensitive ears creates its own problem – equivalent to putting a sensitive microphone next to a firing cannon – the power of the sound is liable to damage the bats' ears. To overcome this difficulty they decouple the delicate bones in their ears when they make the noise. Evolution has provided them a means of switching off their ears when they issue their ultrasonic blasts.

The bats get even more information from frequency modulating (changing the pitch of) their sounds and from the Doppler effect (the change in pitch of the echo caused by the motion of the source relative to the receiver) enabling them to follow the movement of the moths they prey upon. They even filter out the babble of the other bats in their vicinity (in large caverns it could be millions) by relating the picture they get each time their ears switch on to the previous one. This is analogous to the method used by astronomers searching for new features in photographs of the night sky. A photographic plate of part of the sky is compared with an identical plate taken previously. Comparing the plates side by side is tedious and prone to error because of the millions of stars on the plates. Instead each photograph is projected into the astronomer's visual field in quick succession. Any object present on one but absent on the other immediately reveals itself by winking – thus is found a nova. If something has moved it seems to be jumping backwards and forwards – thus a comet or asteroid is found. The background "noise" of millions of fixed stars remains static and unnoticed, effectively removed by a technique perfected in its auditory context by the poor bat. All this is done quite spontaneously and unconsciously by the bat just as we are not conscious of the way we get pictures of the world via our eyes. Dawkins believes the bat has a mental picture of its surroundings based on its auditory sense in every way as complete as ours based on our visual sense.

Some bats, the flying foxes, lack this elaborate sonar equipment though they may have a cruder version of it. They are also different from insectivorous bats in other ways. They are much larger with wingspans up to five feet, they live in trees rather than belfries and, of course, they eat fruit not insects. These differences suggest they might have evolved the bat wing independently of their insectivorous, echo-sounding brethren – another example of evolutionary convergence.

The whale has an unusually large brain probably because, like the bat, it has its own three dimensional map of the world's oceans which it constantly updates from its own echolocation system. It also talks to its fellow creatures. Tests on captive dolphins show the sophistication of their sonar system. They can distinguish objects of the same size by their shapes – a triangle from a square, for example. And they can detect a sphere half the size of a golf ball at 70 yards by sonar alone. All cetaceans use echolocation but baleen whales like the blue whale probably evolved independently of the toothed whales like the dolphin, further cases of convergence.

Alternative location systems evolve when the normal visual system cannot work efficiently – bats flying at night, birds nesting in deep caves, whales in deep waters and fish living in muddy estuaries. Two groups of fish have evolved location systems based on electric fields, yet are quite unrelated species. One group lives in African waters, the other in South American. Both groups of electric fish use the same design principles for their location systems. Muscles along the fish's flanks generate a weak electromagnetic field which surrounds the fish. Detectors also along their flanks monitor its intensity. In open water the field is symmetrical and corresponding detectors to the left and to the right register the same value. If any object comes within range of the field however it upsets the symmetry and the fish becomes aware of it from slight differences in voltage to the left and to the right.

But this solution to the problem of "seeing" in murky water generates another. Any movement of the body of the fish would create an asymmetry in the field yielding information only about the fish's bodily movements – the fish has to be rigid. How then is it to swim? A long fin running the length of its rigid body evolved – by undulating the fin the fish could swim while keeping its body stiff. Proof that the two fish evolved quite separately is that the fin of the African fish is on its back while that of the South American version is on its underside. Furthermore both groups have some members that regenerate their fields in discontinuous pulses and some that use a sort of alternating current. Not only have the two groups independently evolved the same location system but members of each group have separately evolved the same two methods of replenishing their electromagnetic fields.

There are other types of electric fish altogether more fearsome – the strongly electric fish which electrocute their victims by issuing a powerful electrical discharge. The electric eel is one such fish and the electric ray another. They are unrelated and must have developed their electrical weaponry independently. Indeed they have evolved quite different solutions to their other evolutionary problems. The electric eel is not an eel (it is related to the carp) but has adopted the eel shape because of its narrow habitat among rocks on the sea bed. The electric ray is a cartilaginous fish related to the shark but adapted for feeding on flat sandy ocean floors, whence its flat shape.

The African mormyrid's electric field allows it to sense its surroundings in muddy water. Fascinatingly, it has evolved a greatly enlarged cerebellum, strangely reminiscent of the mammal's neocortex, apparently because of its novel sense system. These electric fish might even communicate via their electric fields. Electric fields are really electromagnetic fields – they always have magnetic fields associated with them – and when they oscillate they generate electromagnetic radiation in a spectrum ranging from high frequency cosmic rays to low frequency radio waves. In its muddy waters the fish is using the low frequency end of the spectrum. We have a fish that is communicating by radio. And, to help it do it, it is developing a brain. What price the intelligent mammal being succeeded by an intelligent, telepathic fish?

Of the many other examples of convergent features are mundane ones like webbed toes in a wide variety of vertebrates adapted to watery lives such as ducks, beavers, otters, frogs, crocodiles and quite often in humans. Then there are highly specialized ones like the filtering devices used by some creatures for sieving tiny shrimps and krill from water. Species as different as whales, sharks and flamingos all use the same technique today but there are also extinct examples. A long legged duck developed the filtering system 45 million years ago in North America and in Argentina a pterodactyl fed in the same way.

So much for the evolution of particular specialized features in different animals but the general features of animals, in common or similar environments, can also evolve convergently. Grass or scrub is poor in readily assimilated nutrients. To get sufficient nutrition the animals have to eat a lot, and they need a way of breaking down the tough food. To help their digestion, many, like the cow, have bacteria in their gut which ferment cellulose. To process large amounts of poor quality food and intimidate potential predators some grow to large sizes – like the rhino and elephant. To evade predators many become very nimble growing long legs to improve their speed and effectively lengthening their limbs by standing on their toes – like horses and gazelle.

The cracking apart of the Southern supercontinent of Gondwanaland starting about 130 million years ago provided us with a huge natural experiment in evolution. Ultimately South America, Africa and Australia were to separate and remain separate for countless aeons allowing evolution to take its course on three large landmasses independently. We can see the results of this experiment both in the flesh and in the fossil record. A pronounced example was that of the litopterns which evolved on the grasslands of South America. Faced with an identical environment to that of horses, the litopterns evolved legs so astonishingly like horses' legs that one expert was convinced that the horse actually evolved in South America. "Grassland life is much the same the world over, and horses and litopterns independently evolved the same qualities to cope," observes Richard Dawkins.

South America also produced marsupial equivalents of rhinos, elephants and camels but most of the native South American species were out-competed when a link was formed with the North American continent allowing placental mammals to invade. And we have met these features in studying the dinosaurs. The problems faced by herbivorous dinosaurs then were similar to those posed to grassland herbivores today. Sauropods were dinosaur elephants; ceratopsians were dinosaur rhinos; hadrosaurs were dinosaur cattle or horses, as shown by their obvious features as well as by the ratios of the bones in their legs. In Australia the grassland herbivores, the kangaroos and wallabies, quite different from horses or gazelles are uncannily similar in appearance to some dinosaurs.

The marsupial sugar glider is very similar to the primitive coluga or the North American flying squirrel, while the marsupial mole looks remarkably similar to the placental mole. Australia and South America had no true native cats or dogs but parallels between some marsupial and placental carnivores are so close that it is not easy to tell them apart without a careful examination. There have been marsupial wolves in Australia and marsupial cats in South America. The marsupial wolf or thylacine only died out 50 years ago. Indeed there are repeated claims that breeding groups still live in remote parts of Tasmania and Australia. Newsreels from the 1930s show us exactly what it was like – virtually indistinguishable from a dog.

Some lowly creatures, the anteaters, were moulded in the Gondwanaland experiment. These creatures developed long noses with long sticky tongues and strong claws for breaking into ants' and termites' nests. Australia has a marsupial anteater with just these characteristics and also has the spiny anteater, a burrowing monotreme like the duck-billed platypus. Africa and Asia have placental anteaters like the aardvark and the pangolin. South America has placental anteaters suited to different habitats but which are more similar in external appearance to the marsupial editions in Australia than their closer cousins in Africa. An interesting common feature is their low metabolic rate which gives them an unusually low body temperature. We have noted this in the platypus, with its only semi-warm blood. But a low metabolic rate in this variant group of creatures, differing in many ways other than in their adaptation to a diet of ants, suggests that their diet provides some other evolutionary constraint. Convergent evolution responded with a low metabolic rate.

Within ants themselves there are many cases of parallel evolution but particularly striking is the parallel between the army ants of South America and the driver ants of tropical Africa. Both types periodically move camp lock, stock and barrel, swarming across the countryside carrying their queen or queens, larvae and eggs and sweeping all before them. The African variety moves in the largest numbers – about 20 million ants weighing some 45 pounds take to the road. In South America the colonies might have about a million individuals. These species of ants have evolved their peculiar habits quite separately on two different continents.

Convergent evolution is also exemplified by comparing the lifestyles and appearances of ants and termites. Although termites are totally unrelated to ants, being more the kin of cockroaches, their popular name, white ants, betrays the perceived similarities. Both ants and termites have evolved into many biological niches. Some species of both groups have become mushroom farmers taking decaying vegetation into their colonies to grow fungus which they then use as food. Each fungus has become so specialized that it can only survive with the help of the insects.

Workers of both ants and termites are sterile to maintain the cohesion of the colony. By allowing only the queen and her consorts to procreate there can be no division of loyalty within the nest. If more evidence were needed that the habits of both groups do not stem from a common ancestor, it is that all ants' workers are sterile females whereas the termites' workers are both males and females.

We have seen that animals similar to modern ones evolved by convergence among extinct species too. Besides triceratops and the rhino there are examples like struthiomimus and the ostrich, ichthyosaurs and whales, and pterosaurs and birds or bats. Convergence at the time of the dinosaurs to solutions which are still suitable today confirms that many evolutionary problems were broadly the same, even though elements of the environment characteristic of today, such as grass, had not emerged in the Cretaceous period. Many of the solutions discovered by the mammals had already been discovered by the dinosaurs before them. Perhaps more than we have imagined!

You might be wondering how the environment brings about changes, convergent or otherwise, in animals. It is helpful to know the gist of how evolution works.

There are three driving forces of evolution.

- Overpopulation. Far more creatures are born than survive to adulthood. Those that fail to breed are either unlucky (a random factor) or are not suited to their environment in some respect, however small.
- Variation. Not all creatures are the same and even small differences can be important to survival.
- Inheritance. Animals pass on their innate characteristics to their young.

From these you can see that an animal born into a particular environment with certain characteristics inherited from its parents and adequately suited to its environment will survive to breed and give birth to a new generation which will inherit its characteristics. The cycle continues – the species survives. Another animal is badly adapted to it environment, say a black polar bear or a mute blackbird. It is unlikely to breed successfully and the variant feature that led to its failure will not have the chance of appearing again in the next generation. Black polar bears and mute blackbirds quickly die out.

These examples illustrate selection against gross differences in features but Darwin regarded evolution as occurring through an accumulation of small changes caused by the selection of small variations inherited from parents. Such small variations do not prevent breeding, but tip the scales slightly. A grey polar bear might be able to pass on its greyness for many generations because ninety nine times out of a hundred it is as successful in catching seals as its white rivals. But that one time out of a hundred that the white bears are more successful than the grey ones will ensure that the population of polar bears will eventually be all white. Over generations of natural selection that tiny difference favors the white variety.

In Darwinian evolutionary theory, evolution should occur gradually and the gradual changes should be visible in the fossil record. They rarely are. Darwin was unhappy that there was not a smoother fossil record. Species seemed rather to live unchanged for a long time then change suddenly to something new. Eldredge and Gould's theory of punctuated evolution explained this apparent anomaly, extending Falconer's ideas of a hundred years before. When it is well adapted to a stable environment a species can experience a long period of stability. But then it suddenly evolves very quickly, perhaps within ten to a hundred generations. Since geologists can rarely measure intervals in the rocks of closer than 100,000 years, such a rapid change occurs in too short a period to leave a fossil record. It seems as though one species had suddenly given way to the newer one.

Dawkins calculates that in 60,000 years an animal the size of a mouse (40g) could evolve into an animal the size of an elephant (6,000,000g). In 12,000 generations of an average five years per generation, a rate of growth of 0.02 per cent per generation would effect the change yet would be too small for any contemporary observer to notice. Yet in the geological record mice will have given way to elephants in adjacent strata. The change would appear instantaneous in the rocks.

According to Ernst Mayr, it is isolation that allows one branch to evolve quickly in response to the new set of conditions while the larger original group remains fairly stable. Mayr defined a species as "a group of interbreeding natural populations that are reproductively isolated from other such groups". Polar bears and brown bears can allegedly breed together to give birth to fertile offspring. In this respect they are both of the same species. But, of course, they never meet in the wild because they live in widely different habitats – they are reproductively isolated and are classified as different species. Reproductive isolation does not necessarily mean that mating never occurs between the two relatively isolated groups of animals but its frequency must be low. Eventually, as speciation progresses, the offspring become infertile even when mating does occur. Polar bears might occasionally meet brown bears, in Alaska perhaps, and they could interbreed on those occasions.

But the frequency of such occurrences is low indeed. Eventually brown and polar bears will not yield fertile young even if they are able to crossbreed. Then the two lines of bears will have been forever separated.

Horses and donkeys mating to give birth to mules is another example. Donkeys and horses have a common ancestor but donkeys specialized for life in rocky deserts while horses specialized in temperate grasslands. Their common ancestor was probably a horse so donkeys are horses that have begun to evolved differently because of their different environment. Now, they cannot interbreed because the product of their union is the sterile mule or hinny. Some of the minority and the main populations, chancing to meet, might attempt to reproduce by mating but the next generation is infertile so reproductive isolation is complete.

A group of individuals isolated from the main population for long enough eventually becomes a new species. Suppose the new species again came into contact with the parent population – perhaps the sea level had risen isolating some animals on a small island but then it fell again. If the new animals had advantages over the old that had evolved in isolation, then they would rapidly dominate the parent population, possibly pushing them to extinction for their conservatism. The original isolated group would have left only a localized fossil record of their evolution on that small island. In later years, unless by luck that particular region were prospected, no fossils showing their evolution would be found. The main group, on the other hand, being widespread, would have left fossils widely dispersed and easy to discover. Having overwhelmed the old, the new variety would become widespread and its fossils common. Geological strata will show the new species replacing the old instantly in the fossil record. Alternatively the, formerly stable, parent population might be forced to evolve because competition with the invaders is an environmental factor they had not previously encountered. Because competition had forced the original population to change rapidly, the fossil record will again show an apparently discontinuous change.

Darwin recognized from his studies on the Galapagos Islands that chains of islands are perfect for isolating populations to allow speciation to occur. High sea levels cutting off tracts of land provide the nurseries of species. This possibly happened in the evolution of man in the last few million years and it must have happened to some of the dinosaurs in the Cretaceous period when sea levels were high.

One wonders however whether speciation can occur even when populations are not physically isolated in any way. Reproductive isolation is needed. What could promote some of a population to eschew breeding with the rest, if they are not physically isolated? Could there be an incest gene? By conditioning its owner to prefer sex with close relatives and its children could it allow speciation via sexual isolation within a breeding group? The incest gene would make an animal prefer its own kin, perhaps by linking with a gene which expresses itself in some subtle physical feature, recognizable even at a subliminal level by parents and siblings, a pheromone perhaps. If, by breeding together, an incestuous family retains some advantageous characteristic, the incest gene will spread and will ultimately determine a new species to replace the previous one.

The wolf and coyote in North America are interesting examples of close but different species. The wolf commonly hunts in packs whereas the coyote is more solitary. Though present in the same territory, in the wild they do not interbreed and so are classed as different species but in captivity they can be made to interbreed and produce what Bakker describes as healthy hybrids. Was the coyote an incestuous wolf in earlier times?

Strong support for evolution – its fundamental machinery – came with the discovery by Watson and Crick of the double helical structure of the DNA (deoxyribonucleic acid) molecule. DNA is the blueprint of life. It contains in its sequences of nucleotides (nitrogen containing molecules able to form weak but specific bonds with each other) the factors or genes which influence variation and pass on characteristics from one generation to the next. The discovery that DNA was a double helix demonstrated in the most obvious way the basis for reproduction – the helix simply split down the center of its coil forming two separate halves. Each half then reformed the complete molecule from the surrounding nutrient molecules. Thus two complete molecules are formed from one and these can in turn divide and reform, multiplying the molecule as long as there are enough nutrient molecules remaining in the environment.

Astonishingly enough, experiments have been carried out showing that convergence can occur in the replication of molecules like these. RNA (ribonucleic acid) is a fundamental molecule of life related in structure to DNA although simpler. It too is a replicating molecule. Sol Spiegelman extracted RNA from a virus and put it into a test tube with an enzyme (a molecule which helps a biochemical reaction to occur) and some nutrient molecules. The RNA replicated itself. A drop of the resulting liquid was extracted and put into another test tube containing only nutrient molecules and the enzyme. The drop contained some of the RNA molecules so these replicated as before. The same procedure was then repeated exhaustively. The RNA was analyzed at intervals to check its structure.

It was found that the RNA evolved!

Occasionally an error in the replication process occurred to yield a slightly different RNA molecule. If that proved not to be as good at replicating as the rest of them then it soon got diluted to such an extent that the drop extracted from the last test tube contained none of the mutant molecules and that "species" had died out. If however the mutant was better at reproducing itself in the test tube environment than its parent, the converse occurred. Before long the original RNA had become so diluted by the mutant's offspring that the drop taken from the last test tube contained none of the original and the mutant RNA had survived the extinction of the old "species".

After many trials a stable species seemed to evolve – the one best suited to the test tube world in which it lived! Remarkably, the experimenters went on to provide the most spectacular example of convergence. They found that the same RNA molecule evolved from different RNA taken from different sources!

The story is yet more amazing. Manfred Eigen, a Nobel prizewinning chemist, carried out a complementary and even more unlikely experiment. He used no RNA as a "seed" molecule. He just used the enzyme and the nutrient molecular broth. After many trials he found that RNA built itself spontaneously from the nucleotides and other molecules present. It then evolved into essentially the same test tube "species" as before. Its size and general structure were the same but there were some minor variations. Just as you would expect of convergence from considerably different starting points.

So, with overpopulation, variation and inheritance transmitting the effects of the environment to successive generations of creatures, evolutionary change occurs. Because there are a large number of environmental factors, evolution effectively takes place in a multidimensional space in which the factors are the dimensions. C.H.Waddington introduced the concept of epigenetic landscapes moulded by physical laws which determine the possible paths of evolution just as streams flow down valleys in our three dimensional physical landscapes.

There are only certain routes through the multidimensional space that are likely, small deviations from them being unstable and reverting to the original path. A large deviation, though, could displace motion through the space to an alternative route. In physical terms, a small displacement of a spring will not alter the main course of the stream which it generates. It rapidly assumes the lowest point in the valley as it did before and then flows along the same riverbed. But a large displacement could take the outlet of the spring to the other side of the watershed and the course of the stream would then be quite different. It might flow out into a different ocean. Or it might flow down a valley which eventually runs into its previous course as a tributary, convergent evolution – though starting in different places the two rivers eventually flow together.

In this picture, features like echolocation or the camera eye, correspond to lakes in depressions in the landscape perhaps surrounded by high lands cut through by only a few narrow valleys. If evolution should lead into one of these valleys then it is very likely to lead to the lake which is the biological feature, camera eye or whatever. The landscape image offers a way of illustrating convergent evolution. It also offers a useful way of visualizing evolutionary paths as valleys, punctuated evolution as a succession of hanging valleys or tarns and stable features as lakes. At least one such lake in the landscape must correspond to the development of intelligence. We, in our arrogance, believe we are the only species to have bathed in that particular lake, but evolutionary convergence warrants that other species will do so sooner or later. Perhaps they already have.

One route there, is down the evolutionary rapids which we shall consider shortly. First, an example of how convergence theory has been used by some unorthodox thinkers to account for the mysterious gap from eight million to four million years ago in the emergence of man.

CHAPTER SEVEN

SUBMERGENCE CONVERGENCE: THE AQUATIC APE

"We know the way to heaven to be as ready by water as by land."

Elstow

Land animals quite commonly return to the water just as birds sometimes become flightless. Herr Hauff's ichthyosaur evolved from an ancestor that returned to the water over 200 million years ago.

In the last 80 million years mammals have often entered the water, found it comfortable and stayed. The cetaceans, the whales and dolphins, were the first to do it. Little rat-like creatures like all mammals then, they sought to avoid the terrors of the dinosaurs by hiding in the water of river estuaries. It was safer, they stayed and gradually adapted to their new surroundings. The buoyancy and safety afforded by the water allowed them to grow bigger and eventually take to the open sea, especially after the great carnivorous sea dinosaurs had all died. Today they are supremely adapted to the aquatic environment. But occasionally a throwback will reveal something more of the original land mammal.

Some hoofed mammals paddled into the water 50 million years ago to become the dugongs and manatees. About 25 million years ago, a bear-like creature took to the water to evolve into sea lions and at the same time some dog-like mammals immersed themselves to become today's seals. More recently we have seen otters of the stoat family adapt to the water, beavers (a rodent), the hippopotamus only 5 million years ago. And... a certain ape?

Although most zoological orders can boast some representative that has fully adapted to water, the order of primates cannot. Sir Alister Hardy proposed to change that by suggesting in 1960 that many of man's peculiar features could be explained if an ancestor had adapted to an aquatic or semiaquatic life for a few million years before emerging again equipped to conquer the world. Hardy's theory, though gaining adherents, is not regarded as respectable in most anthropological quarters but, if an ape did submerge, there was a very good reason and a likely place for it to happen. More of this toward the end of the chapter.

A few million years in the water give us convincing explanations of otherwise untypical and inexplicable human characteristics, including some of the those we have been looking at. Why are we bipedal? Why are we naked? Why do we have a layer of subcutaneous fat? Why do we possess the diving reflex? Why can young human babies swim before they can walk? What triggered off speech? Writer, Elaine Morgan, expands on Alister Hardy's idea in her book, "The Aquatic Ape", in which she makes a compelling case for the aquatic hypothesis. She takes questions like these and attempts to answer them from the physiology and behavior of known aquatic animals. In other words

75

she uses the principles of convergent evolution – human adaptations typical of aquatic animals suggesting an aquatic origin for humans.

An animal in a given environment is faced with a set of evolutionary problems. To resolve these, it has a limited number of efficient solutions – there are only certain routes in the evolutionary landscape that are feasible. Anteaters, pangolins and aardvarks, all having the same type of lifestyle, have developed the same characteristics, long snouts, strong claws and sticky tongues, to let these creatures dine on colonies of insects. By looking at the common features of these creatures one can deduce that they have similar habits. Their similar solutions to the problems of their environment suggest that environment. If we see an animal with a set of characteristics usually acquired in an environment different from its own, it seems reasonable to deduce that the animal has at some time experienced the environment which gives rise to its peculiar characteristics. The arguments for human origins as an aquatic ape are therefore instructive, highlighting convergence and the features which make us singularly human, but I shall give them very tersely to avoid delay in my own arguments.

Humans are the only mammal habitually to walk on two legs, though some others do occasionally. Grassland animals like the vervet monkey, the rabbit, the meercat and the gopher stretch upright to look around for danger but, if they see any, they run off on all fours. Why don't they stay upright as man has done?

In 1970 C.R.Taylor tried experimentally to show the relative energy cost of walking on two or on four legs. Initially he announced that bipedal walking was twice as expensive in terms of the energy needed. Owen Lovejoy was right – walking bipedally is "preposterous!" Not so. Later, more accurate experiments contradicted Taylor's initial assessment. They still favored four legs but in a more subtle way. The energy cost did not materially differ for two legged and for four legged locomotion. But, for the same energy output, animals could move much faster on four limbs than they could on two.

It looks unlikely that a slow, ungainly tree dweller could succeed in the world of fast moving grazers and predators by attempting to walk upright. Not that a bipedal creature cannot compensate for the speed of its four legged competitors, our own dominance of the world is proof enough of this – the advantages conferred by two legged walking plainly have overcome the advantage of speed – but how could the tyro bipedal ape learn the skills he needed before he got eaten by the fast four legged hunters? The protagonists of the aquatic ape theory are not convinced by the scenario of the savannah ape. They argue that the ape had to have the safety of some haven from the predators to learn how to stand upright and water provided that haven for mankind just as it had for the ancestors of whales and seals. Wading out into the sea to search for seaweed or shellfish is a safe and natural way to become upright.

Macaques, those widespread, intelligent and alert monkeys, seem to be broadening their response to their environment even as we look on. Crab eating macaques are one of the few primates that do not fear water: they wade out into the sea to catch their crunchy prey. Japanese macaques, we saw, discovered how to wash sandy potatoes in the sea, wading out on their hind legs while holding the potatoes. If these animals were to wade out of their depth they would find that they floated upright quite naturally – as a man does. Beavers, having got used to an upright position when resting in the water, find it useful sometimes to walk on their hind legs when carrying their young or materials for dam building.

Many sea mammals habitually float upright in the water – like the manatee. Female manatees have rounded, human-looking breasts and sit upright in the water cradling their young in their "arms" whilst suckling them. Steller's sea cow behaved similarly before men hunted it to extinction. These are the only other mammals to have developed anything like human breasts. Seen from a distance bobbing upright in the water with their breasts exposed, sometimes with a baby in their arms, perhaps draped in the weed upon which they fed, they excited the imagination of lonely sailors and gave rise to the legend of the mermaid. When swimming, however, these creatures launch themselves horizontally. A creature that walks on two legs, the penguin, swims horizontally and another creature that walks on two legs also swims horizontally – man. The effect on the seal of adapting to the horizontal swimming position was to swing its pelvic girdle parallel to its spine. The same transformation has occurred in man!

The human body is remarkably streamlined, and any moving picture of humans swimming underwater shows immediately how graceful we are in the water. It is the need for streamlining in the relatively dense medium of water that forces a bullet shape on to animals which are habitual swimmers – mankind has been no exception. A consequence of this streamlining is the necessity to copulate in more convenient ways than the normal rear mounting method of most mammals. Man is the only great ape to copulate face-to-face, yet the majority of marine mammals do so. It has required the human female to orient her sexual canals towards the front. Female foetuses of apes, but not adult females, have their sexual canals oriented towards the front. Human females carry this feature into adulthood. Such a change, foetal or infantile characteristics taken into adulthood, is called neoteny.

Amphibians begin life in the water as tadpoles but as adults spend most of their time on land. But a Mexican salamander found life in the water more comfortable than the struggle on land and a neotenous change occurred to adapt it for such a life. It kept all the features of its tadpole stage into adult life and actually breeds and lives its whole life now as a large tadpole. It is the axolotl. We know for sure it is a neotenous salamander because it can be induced to undergo the metamorphosis that it normally postpones for life and the result is an ordinary looking salamander.

Neoteny is a mechanism for rapid adaptation to changing conditions and succeeds because juveniles are usually less specialized than adults. A minor change to a gene controlling development is all that is needed to delay growing up. It seems to have worked strongly in man's evolution. Those who dislike the aquatic theory say that neoteny is all that is needed to explain the changes in the developing ape. If so, what unusual conditions required neotenous changes in an ape setting out to explore the grasslands? Evidently none. The baboon successfully made the same transition without invoking neoteny. Indeed its snout lengthened compared with an ordinary monkey rather than remaining flat like the foetal baboon's. Nor did they lose their body hair as mankind did. Admittedly, man is not really the "naked ape" because he has as many hair follicles per unit area as any other great ape. Human beings look naked because human hairs are so short and so fine that, to all intents and purposes, human beings are naked. Why should a savannah ape be effectively naked? What is the reason for human nakedness?

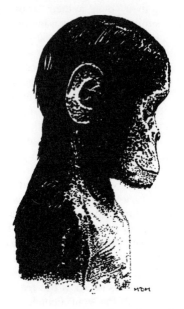

Exhibit 5. Neoteny illustrated by the flat, almost human face of a baby chimpanzee

Some anthropologists argue that by shedding hair our ancestors were able to keep cooler whilst hunting. Who then did the hunting? Human females? Female humans have lost more hair than male humans. And if nakedness solved the problem of overheating, why did other mammals not adapt in the same way? Other primates which took to the grasslands when the Miocene forests retreated, like vervet monkeys as well as baboons, did not find it necessary to lose their hair. Indeed, why, if nakedness is held to be such an advantage, do many humans, like the bedouin, cover their skins with wrappings of loose cloth in strong sunlight? Hair protects the skin from direct solar radiation and it also acts as an insulator, by trapping air, keeping its owner warm on cold savannah nights. Hairless humans have to use warm blankets at night to substitute for their ineffective hair. It is strange for any creature of the savannah to be bald unless they have thick skin like the elephant or the rhinoceros.

Other savannah theorists sidestep this reasoning, accepting that nakedness was disadvantageous but arguing that neoteny nonetheless effected the change because the advantages outweighed the disadvantages. The foetuses of great apes are, at one stage of their development, naked. A trigger is needed for neoteny to have occurred but it was not entering the water – it was to accommodate the human learning experience. Maturity was delayed so that an extended childhood could fill the growing brain with knowledge and experience. Gestation, childhood and progress to maturity slowed down relative to other primates; childhood features were retained including childhood curiosity which gave humans the incentive to learn late into their lives. The extension of adult life also meant that parents survived long enough to protect and teach their slow maturing offspring. But neoteny cannot choose the good features of the infant to extend into adulthood and leave unchanged the others. The whole gamut of juvenile features have to be carried into adulthood. Though hairlessness was disadvantageous, the package was advantageous overall and was selected by natural selection.

But this whole notion is easily disproved, first by the success of other primates successfully stepping on to the grasslands at the same time without recourse to neotenous changes, and second by the lanugo of human babies which is overlooked by the savannah theorists. The lanugo is the hairy covering that human foetuses have before birth. They start to become hairy but the hair regresses, and by birth has usually gone, though, on occasions it is retained for a while after birth, to the horror of some parents. The neotenous changes envisaged by the savannah theorists would surely have favored selection of the lanugo to continue into adult life to protect the hominid's sunboiled skin and retain warmth in the cool nights. We should quickly have been no longer the naked ape. The failure of the lanugo to evolve as a protection shows that human nakedness evolved as a positive response to some situation. Living in water was it.

Creatures which commonly do lose their hair, quite naturally because it is favorable to their evolution, are animals that spend all or part of their time in water. The longer the evolutionary period they are immersed, the more likely they are to be bald. The hypothesis of the aquatic ape is that mankind is naked because we lived for several million years as partly aquatic creatures. The hippopotamus which evolved at about the same time as man, only five and a half million years ago, is naked, though it does not spend its whole time in the water. It emerges, usually at night.

Fur is primarily a heat insulator to retain the warmth of the warm-blooded mammals, though strictly it is not the fur itself which insulates, it is the air trapped by the fur. Wet fur is useless as an insulator. The trapped air is replaced by water, a better conductor of heat, which renders the fur ineffective. Hair also slows down a swimming animal because it creates friction in the denser medium. Though humans are hardly hairy, this friction can be so crucial that swimming champions shave their body hair before a race to gain a fraction of a second on less competitive rivals who have not bothered. Mammals that have retained hair despite living in water return to the land to breed and live in colder northerly climates where their fur is still useful for insulation when the animal is out of the water. Seals, sea lions, beavers and otters are in this category.

So, human hairlessness can be explained by a few million years' dip. But why do humans, especially human females have thick hair on their heads? Because hair on the scalp served as protection against the tropical sun when the apes were floating upright in the water. Their naked bodies were protected by the water but not the tops of their heads. A woman's hair tends to be more permanent than a man's, but more interesting is that it gets stronger and thicker in pregnancy. Elaine Morgan believes aquatic children needed to hang on to their mothers in the water. Baby monkeys cling to their mother's fur, but if all the hair had gone from the aquatic ape its baby would have been in trouble, instinctively trying but failing to cling on to smooth slippery skin. What is more natural than scalp hair, retained to prevent burnt heads, providing an anchor for babies?

Hairlessness could have served to allow the hominids and the australopithecines to distinguish themselves when the two lines were still evolutionarily and geographically close. Those in the hominid line might have selected sexual partners that were hairless while, in the other line, hairiness might have been the factor chosen. Each would find the appearance of their close relatives repugnant. This is sexual selection. Darwin recognized it as being an important selection mechanism.

But Morgan argues that sexual selection in favor of a feature can occur in a species only when that feature has already become established for other reasons. Once the aquatic ape became naked through cavorting in the water, sexual selection would ensure that nakedness continued. In like manner, the aquatic apes would not regard the retention of scalp hair as ugly. It would be regarded as a supremely attractive feature. Nowadays men and women alike regard women with beards with fascination and horror, but they admire beautifully coiffured scalp hair on women. Smooth skin in a man is not regarded by women as ugly, perhaps the opposite, but a bald pate they often think is unattractive – on women, generally admired for their smoothness, it is worse. These instances seem illogical unless sexual selection in the aquatic context is considered.

Frowning is a peculiarly human habit, explained by the aquatic hypothesis as a response to the sun's glare from the surface of the water. But, except in their faces, humans have largely lost the muscles which move their skin. Vestiges remain in phenomena like scalp hair standing on end through fear, and cold causing goose pimples, but we have nothing like the ability cows or horses have to shake off flies by vigorously twitching their skin. The skin muscles were lost along with hair because moving hair was their main function: no hair, no skin muscles – they had become redundant. The retention of muscles to move the skin in the face is connected with visual communication. Animals floating upright at the water's surface only had their faces exposed. Interpretation of subtle facial movements therefore took on special significance. The expression of emotions via facial expressions would have been especially important as social structure evolved.

A layer of fat underneath the skin is a much better insulator than fur for a warm-blooded water dweller. No primate has it – except man. It is another peculiarly human feature. Some other terrestrial animals store fat but rarely under their skin. Humans are born with a fat layer. Human babies are unusually rounded, and heavier than the babies of the great apes. A human baby is almost twice as heavy as a baby gorilla or chimpanzee though human adults are lighter. According to the aquatic theory, besides providing necessary insulation to the baby this fat was a vital aid to buoyancy.

Other mammals besides man have sweat glands which they use for excretion of wastes. Man is unusual in having exceptional numbers of them, and in using them as a way of keeping cool. Sweat cools by taking away body heat as latent heat of vaporization. It requires free access of air to the skin since air trapped near the skin soon becomes saturated in moisture. Further evaporation then stops and sweating no longer works. Hairiness stops sweating from being efficient as a cooling system. No great ape, other than man, sweats to keep cool. It would be inefficient if it did. But for sweating to evolve as a means of keeping cool on dry or even arid grasslands is absurd – it drains the body of essential water and salts. And it would be suicidal for any ape to opt for a water cooling system where water is at a premium – on the dry grasslands. A man walking naked in the tropical sun at 100 degrees Fahrenheit (40 degrees Celsius) can lose up to 28 liters of fluid and an eighth of his body's salt a day by sweating. For urination only one liter is needed.

It is plain nonsense to postulate that the savannah ape first lost its hair to keep cool, then put on a subcutaneous layer of fat to keep warm and finally developed a life threatening system of sweating to keep cool again. The only way to make sense of such a ridiculous sequence is the aquatic hypothesis. The first two stages, hair loss and the evolution of a fat layer instead, were adaptations to living in water. Sweating served two purposes. It was a way of ridding the body of surplus salt ingested while foraging in the sea. And it was a natural way of allowing a water ape to keep comfortable when out of the water by taking a little of its environment with it.

The loss of large amounts of water would not matter if a water supply is always nearby, and so aquatic apes would not have willingly moved away from their water source. Their gradual re-adaptation to the land would have been by them staying close to rivers and lakes and moving inland only as their sophistication grew.

We have seen how close we are to the chimpanzees in terms of DNA. We are also similar in our thought processes. Chimpanzees have a wide range of emotions and have sufficiently mobile faces to show them. But when distressed they do not cry, simply because they cannot, despite their evolutionary closeness to humans. Only elephants and humans of land animals express tears. All other animals that weep are aquatic. (And there is a lot of evidence that elephants were aquatic at some time long ago!) It is a poignant sight to see a baby seal after its mother has been clubbed to death by a human with a baseball bat, weeping on the ice floes before it too has its skull crushed, killed to gratify human vanity. Birds, particularly marine birds, have nasal glands behind their beaks to get rid of excess salt, but these birds also get a wet beak from the salt gland when they are excited or emotionally aroused. They are crying. Other marine creatures such as the marine turtles, marine iguanas and terrapins have similar glands. Crocodiles do cry crocodile tears but only the marine variety, not river crocodiles which do not have to cope with salty water.

Many dinosaurs had spaces in their skulls in front of their eye sockets and these are thought to have housed similar salt glands. So it is possible that some dinosaurs also cried. The connection of tears with the salt gland and the sea seems obvious, even if its original use is no longer applicable. Only the idea of the aquatic ape can begin to explain a human's ability to cry.

Marine mammals have a most valuable reflex action when they go into a dive. Since they cannot breathe while underwater, they have to conserve oxygen. Their heart beat therefore automatically slows down. This is the diving reflex. Animals that are best adapted to the water, like the cetaceans, show it strongest, and, as far as anyone can tell, the reflex is not present in terrestrial species – though any poor creature thrown into deep water is likely to miss a heartbeat or two, so experimental results are not always conclusive. But, although man is terrestrial, he has a noticeably effective diving reflex. The heartbeat of a diving human slows down to half its normal rate of 72 beats per minute. This is an odd adaptation for a land animal!

Since the diving reflex is a mechanism for coping with a deficiency of oxygen, it has another aspect. It preferentially supplies oxygen to the brain which is soon damaged by lack of it. To do so more robust parts of the body are deprived of oxygen. This explains how people can sometimes be resuscitated after apparently drowning, especially in cold water, without suffering brain damage.

Not all adaptations to diving have proved beneficial to mankind. Asthma is unknown in apes but in humans it mimics the constriction of the bronchial tubes in a diving seal. Diving is, of course, a stress. Asthma looks like a partial adaptation to diving that now manifests itself not under the stress of diving but under the different kinds of stress to which modern humans are subjected.

Human noses are also partially adapted to an aquatic life. They have become narrow, are supported at the tip by a bridge of cartilage, and have nostril flaps with muscles allowing them to be flared. A seal's nostrils have similar muscles that are relaxed when the seal is submerged keeping its nostrils closed. On surfacing the muscles flex and the nostrils open to let the seal breathe. Plainly human forebears had begun to evolve the same means of preventing water from entering their breathing tubes.

Besides their developing ability to close their breathing tubes externally via the nostrils, humans can also block their nasal passages from their throat at will. This aspect of the aquatic adaptation has become an essential feature of speaking. It allows a subtle control of the expulsion of air over the larynx without which speech would be impossible. Thus the control of breathing required by a diving animal has helped humans to develop the power of speech by controlling the passage of breath through the larynx.

Rudimentary webbing can be seen between most people's fingers and especially between the thumb and forefinger, but in about seven per cent of people it is pronounced enough to be regarded as ugly. Why should a line of mammals that have spent 60 or 70 million years in trees show even the slightest trace of webbing, an aquatic adaptation? There is no reason. Webbed hands are useful only for swimming.

Water compulsively attracts human babies. If babies younger than ten months old are put on a gentle slope leading into water they show every sign of being fascinated by this beautiful wet stuff. They explore the new medium, venture into it, show no signs of fear or panic, gaze about in wonderment with their heads underwater, are naturally buoyant, naturally hold their breath for long periods, naturally adopt a swimming position and quickly learn how to swim. After ten months these instincts are lost, the breath control goes because the child has not had cause to develop it. Older children and adults have to be taught how to swim.

Babies have been happily born underwater with apparent benefit to mother and child. Furthermore all terrestrial female mammals, even those that do not eat meat, eat their placenta after childbirth. Human mothers do not, and don't seem inclined to, even if primitive or starving. Aquatic mammals also do not eat their placenta. They have lost the instinct simply because, after the aquatic birth, the afterbirth floats away to be lost while the mother is ministering to the needs of her new born child.

The coordination of group hunting as the drive behind the evolution of speech does not hold water. Mammals like wolves, hyenas and lions hunt cooperatively but have not evolved speech. Watch humans hunting. Far from shouting to each other they communicate by visual signals so as not to forewarn the game (or, in warfare, the enemy). Other than man the creatures that have developed vocal communication furthest are the whales and dolphins. The reason is that visual communication is hampered by the water. Dolphins have a wide range of sounds, many being whistles. If two dolphins start whistling at the same time, one will stop until its companion finishes, then it will resume. It seems as though they are taking it in turns to listen to each other and to speak – they seem to be conversing. But is there any proof?

In behavior experiments, dolphins are not allowed to see each other but are allowed to hear. Yet if one is shown a lever to press to get a reward the other one knows too. They seem to be telling each other which levers to press to be rewarded. Richard Mark Martin concludes, "tasks... were accomplished by the dolphins with so much assurance that it was obvious they did indeed have a language..."

Humpback whales, which can articulate about 20 different sounds, are so sophisticated in language that they "speak" in rhyme. Two US researchers, Linda Guinee and Katherine Payne, came to this conclusion after listening to countless hours of taped humpback whale sounds. A third of the whales' song consisted of rhyming sections. Consecutive passages tend to end in similar sounds even though the rest of the song is quite different. Whales in one part of the ocean use the same rhymes but the rhymes change with time, showing that they are not instinctive like birdsong. Humans find rhymes so compelling that they cannot get certain rhymes and jingles out of their heads. Advertisers play strongly on this. Possibly the rhymes help the whales to remember the songs which act as social cement within the groups. For whales, the rhymes are most common in the more complicated songs – the ones most difficult to remember.

R.D.Martin suggests "there might have been a close association between increasing locomotor sophistication and increase in brain size in primate evolution." Yet in stepping down from a three dimensional life in the trees to a two dimensional life on the plains, surely opportunities for movement were lost, and with it locomotor sophistication would have been decreased. But if the ape first took to the water thus retaining a sense of the vertical while requiring the development of entirely new locomotor skills, Martin's suggestion would have more validity. Animals that take to water often have unusually large brain:body ratios. The talapoin monkey of Gabon is one of the few primates to have taken to water and it has a large brain:body ratio.

Stimulated in the trees, stimulated anew by the transition to water, stimulated again by a whole host of new experiences on moving permanently to the land, the human brain became sophisticated enough to develop, not only locomotor skills but speech, advanced toolmaking and a complex social life that might have had the biggest effect of all.

"Many other primates have moved from the trees to the open plains, and in no single one of them has that move produced any of the changes that caused the ancestors of Homo sapiens to diverge so dramatically from all his nearest relatives", concludes Elaine Morgan. Submergence convergence provides a more convincing explanation.

That is the theory of the aquatic ape in a nutshell. It is not based on fossil evidence. Coastal waters and lowland swamps are not particularly conducive to fossilization. Sharks, crocodiles and crabs would see to that. It is entirely deduced from structural convergence as a plausible explanation of the peculiarities of our species of ape – and the coincidence of suitable geological events.

According to the aquatic theory, a period of immersion for mankind's rootstock produced adaptations that now characterize mankind and differentiate them from their brothers, the apes – loss of body hair, subcutaneous fat, bipedalism, face-to-face sex, sweating, tears and speech. Though not all man's characteristics should be attributed to the aquatic phase, long legs in humans have mainly evolved in the last four million years while the hominids have been walking on land. Lucy had quite short legs.

Why should all this be? – most primates hate water. Gorillas do so to such an extent that a shallow moat is all that is needed to keep them confined. How is it possible that strong adaptation to water occurred? Why should our predecessors have spent a lot of time in it? Where and when did the pre-hominid apes take to the water? When? When the sea level rose flooding the sea margins. The apes had to adapt to water as the lowland forests became swamps and islands, then coastal waters. Similar events in the past put whales, manatees and seals into the water. Where? Where a region isolated by the sea in the Pliocene was populated by apes in the Miocene.

In the late Miocene, movements of crustal plates had opened the narrow but widening Red Sea. Africa and Arabia were still just connected by the Afar Isthmus between what are now Abyssinia and The Yemen. The ape, ramapithecus, lived in Kenya from 14 to 12 million years ago and remains have been found in India dating from 12 to nine million years ago. For part or all of this time, ramapithecus must have lived near the isthmus. At the same time, crustal movements were thrusting up a portion of the earth's surface to form the Danakil Alps. Then, sometime between 6.7 and 5.4 million years ago, the Indian Ocean broke through to the Red Sea flooding the Afar Triangle, where Don Johanson later found Lucy, leaving the Danakil Alps as an island. Danakil island became an evolutionary forcing house for hominid development.

From the end of the Miocene the climate began to become cooler and drier, killing off the forests of Danakil. The forest apes trapped on the island had to adapt to the water, if they had not already done so, because of the scarcity of terrestrial resources and to escape from predators which were better able to cope in the less dense bush of the thinning forests. Present day talapoin monkeys have a strategy of dropping out of the trees into water at any sign of danger. When the lowlands flooded, perhaps the Danakil apes also took to the water by developing the habit of diving out of trees into the swamp or river.

In fact, the Danakil region was probably never a true island. The southern part was probably linked to the African mainland, but extensive volcanic action caused by the movement apart of the Nubian and the Arabian crustal plates created immense lava fields which would have been a daunting barrier to apes moving towards the mainland. But the eruptions would have been episodic: in the quiescent periods the apes might have had chances to escape. This could explain the apparent waves of new hominids appearing quite suddenly throughout mankind's emergence.

In the first quiescent period some of the apes (A.afarensis) were able to cross to the mainland. Others remained behind still evolving. They (Homo habilis) were able to cross about 1.8 million years ago. Then about one million years ago more apes (Homo erectus) crossed. The cycle possibly continued until the region finally dried out about 30,000 years ago, explaining the successive waves of ever more advanced men coming apparently from nowhere and culminating in H.sapiens sapiens.

When the aquatically adapted apes, having escaped from Danakil, began to explore the hinterland, their need for water would have confined their range to waterways and lakes. Paleoanthropologists like Richard Leakey and Don Johanson have found fossil hominid remains in just such places. Four million years ago the emergent submergent apes were at Hadar where Johanson found his remains including Lucy. Later they were at Lake Turkana and Koobi Fori where Richard Leakey's teams found their remains. Hypervitaminosis A, a disease caused by an overdose of vitamin A was noted in some of Leakey's fossils. Leakey's interpretation was that the hominid had had too great a predilection for liver, but the richest source of vitamin A is fish, suggestive of a diet excessively rich in fish to which the ape had not fully adapted.

In the brief period since the forest ape took to the water, according to the scenario just described, not more than 6.7 million years ago, intelligence emerged. Geologically that is a short time. Can features evolve so quickly? The answer is a categoric "yes". Mechanisms have evolved which allow quite astonishingly fast evolution and there are probably more to be discovered. The next chapter shows that rapid evolution can occur. It has happened to mammals yielding mankind: it could have happened to the dinosaurs.

CHAPTER EIGHT

GENES AND EXPLOSIVE EVOLUTION

"Naught may endure save mutability."

P.B.Shelley

There have been conflicting views about how easily intelligence evolves. The age old view supported by religious dogmata was that man is unique in all of creation and therefore intelligence is very rare indeed. In contrast, not many years ago a curious equation was bandied about which purported to prove that we are surrounded by life wherever we look in the universe. A proportion of this is bound to become intelligent and so intelligence exists in every direction you look into space.

The view expounded here is that intelligence corresponds with certain troughs in the evolutionary hyperspace, lakes in the evolutionary landscape. They might be very difficult to get to, perhaps via a small number of tortuous narrow valleys, but any species that finds itself evolving into one such valley is likely, sooner or later, to develop intelligence. Intelligence could be unique at the present time, if only man has so far reached one of the lakes, but in principle other species could get there.

H.J.Jerison has introduced the idea of the EQ, the encephalisation quotient. The EQ takes the ratio of the brain weight to the body weight of an animal, and relates it to the average such ratio for a group of comparable animals. An EQ of 1 means that the animal's brain weight to body weight ratio is typical of the group of comparable animals. If its EQ were bigger than 1, it would have a greater weight of brain than an animal typical of its size in the comparison group. EQ is not the same as IQ. Intelligence depends upon other factors besides the relative mass of the brain, such as the speed of transmission of nerve impulses and their shape. But EQ does indicate potential for IQ: the brain power is there if the evolution of the animal is able to find ways of using it. It is a useful proxy for intelligence.

EQ depends upon the ecological niche occupied by the animal. The three dimensional environment of squirrels give them a higher EQ than their rodent relatives, the rats. Insect eating monkeys have a higher EQ than their fruit eating cousins and the latter, in turn, have a higher EQ than leaf eating monkeys. Animals surrounded by food, the leaf eaters, need little brain power to seek it. The fruit eaters have to hunt for their food and need intelligence to find it. Insect eaters have to develop intelligent strategies to capture their prey which itself has the sense to try to escape. In general carnivores have a higher EQ than the herbivores upon which they prey.

For fossil animals fairly reliable estimates of EQ can be made from cranial casts and the size of the whole skeleton. They show that brain size tends to get bigger over time in accordance with Marsh's Law. There are well established explanations for this. One is that intelligence of response is one aspect of the competition between the predator and its prey. Another is sexual selection. This particularly can give rise to exponential – explosive – evolution via positive feedback loops!

Consider the two mechanisms in turn.

Other things being equal, a marginally more intelligent predator will be more successful than its dimmer peers in capturing its prey. The prey caught will be those that are marginally less intelligent than their peers. In the fullness of time, the results in the populations of predator and prey are that intelligence will increase: the predator's through the animal passing on its characteristic intelligence more successfully; the prey's because the less intelligent were less likely to pass on their lack of intelligence. Later generations of herbivores and carnivores are both more intelligent. There is still a balance of power but at a slightly higher level. An evolutionary arms race is taking place with intelligence the superpower weapon. Predator and prey both finish up with a stronger armory but the balance of power is maintained.

Of course intelligence need not be the only weapon. Similar arms races occur in respect of other weapons. An obvious example is provided by tyrannosaurus rex and the ceratopsians both evolving in response to the other as each improved its weaponry. One developed more and more elaborate defences, heavy bony neck frills and long horns, while the other developed more and more sophisticated jaws and teeth for attack. Both also developed quite large brains by popular standards for dinosaurs.

Thus a predator-prey arms race should result in selection for increasing intelligence in both predator and prey and one might expect technological levels of intelligence to emerge quite naturally, even commonly. That the tendency is there is unequivocal but that high intelligence develops commonly might not be true. The answer again lies in the phrase, "other things being equal". They are not equal. And often they interfere with the competitive progress described above. At the extreme one could not imagine two separate intelligent species evolving in mutual contact. Whichever was the more advanced would rapidly eliminate the other. It seems this happened in the evolution of mankind... possibly several times. Nevertheless, there is a tendency towards selection for intelligence in all predator-prey interactions. Any such tendency, once established, can be powerfully reinforced by sexual selection.

An organism has to reproduce as individuals before it can survive as a species. If an individual is highly successful but fails to reproduce, its successful characteristics cannot be passed on. Selection is not selection merely to survive but selection to reproduce. It is survival until reproduction that is necessary for the continuation of the species. Darwin's dictum would be better expressed as "reproduction of the fittest" rather than "survival of the fittest."

Reproduction has its own necessities. Creatures must first find suitable mates. Then they must be preferred by their intended mates above other competing members of the species. This element of choice of mate is where sexual selection comes in. Usually it is the female that does the selecting. Why? Dawkins invites us to think of the whole cycle of courtship and mating as a game played each mating season. Impregnation puts the females out of the game because she has to concentrate on giving birth, but not so for the male. He can stay in for another round.

The mating game consists of a first round where the most desirable females select the most desirable males as a mates. The less desirable females are not immediately successful because they also are on the look out for very desirable partners. They delay their choice hoping for a desirable mate but tend not to be chosen while there are some of the best females still around. Having secured a desirable mate, the desirable females become pregnant and drop out of the game for the rest of this season. The desirable males are then free to rejoin the less desirable males not yet selected by the less desirable females who are still delaying their choice. Of course, while the most desirable males were courting some of the less desirable males and females will have tired of looking for perfection and will have also paired off. The females remaining are not so desirable but the most desirable males returning to the mating game will again have their pick of them.

The desirable males play the field. The net effect of this is that some of the other males do not get mates because the most desirable ones have had several goes and each time a female is eliminated from the game. The least desirable males do not breed. Males are selected for their desirability, whatever it is. The obvious advantage to a male of being desirable is that he can impregnate several of the females thus passing on his genes and his particular brand of desirability. The males that fail to attract a mate do not pass on their genes. On the other hand females have little need to evolve obviously desirable traits. They only have one turn and even the "undesirable" ones will be in demand by desirable males when all the more attractive females are pregnant.

The females then are normally the sex that does the choosing, needing not to be unusually desirable as long as they are not repugnant. The males benefit by being desirable in some way. Whatever is desirable about them will tend to be enhanced by sexual selection because those that are insufficiently endowed with it have no offspring.

Many characteristics or qualities of individuals within a species, such as height in humans, do not depend upon the interaction of only one gene with the environment but upon many acting together. These are called polygenes. Female preference is a characteristic controlled by a polygene. So also is the set of male features that the female finds rather alluring. The main point of such features are that they are continuous rather than having discrete values.

Consider a male hairy chest. Woman tend to find hairy chests, to a greater or lesser degree, attractive or repugnant. Chests themselves can, of course, be, to a greater or lesser extent, hairy. Some women may have genes giving them a preference for chests which are to a degree hairy while others may be endowed with a preference for the more smooth chested males. If, for some reason, the preference for smooth chests became dominant then the most hairy chested men would find it difficult to find a mate. In the story of the aquatic ape, hydrodynamics determined that smoothness would be advantageous to a swimming primate. The smoother apes would tend to survive and once sexual selection started favoring smoothness then smoothness would prevail even without the influence of the water.

You may protest, "What is to stop women being perverse enough to prefer hairy chested men even though smooth men are in the majority?" The answer is smooth men have the genes for smoothness, plainly enough, but they also have the genes for preferring smoothness. These will be passed on to their daughters who will tend to select smooth chested men as mates! "But why?" you may persist. "Surely a smooth chested man could have the genes for the preference of hairy chests which he would pass on to his daughters." He could. But is he likely to? The answer is no.

A smooth man is more likely to attract a woman who prefers smoothness and a hairy chested man is more likely to attract a woman who prefers hairiness. I am hairy chested like my father. It is more likely – in so far as hairiness was a factor at all in my mother's choice of partner (assume for the sake of this argument that it was) – that my mother preferred hairy chests. It follows that the genes I inherit from my mother are likely to be those for female preference for hairy chests. My daughters will be likely to inherit my mother's preference for hairiness through me or my wife's preference for hairiness (again assuming that my hairiness was influential in my wife's choice of mate).

You can see that hairiness and the preference for hairiness tend to link together through sexual selection. In a species which is predominantly smooth we can be sure that the majority of women prefer smoothness. This linkage of genes is called linkage disequilibrium. When genes are in equilibrium in a population, no particular pairings of genes are favored and the distribution of features is even.

The interesting thing about linkage disequilibrium is that it can form a positive feedback cycle leading to explosive evolution. In the case of smoothness, it could lead to such a selection against hairiness that in a very short period in evolutionary terms, men became smooth – "other things being equal". That all men are not smooth shows that we are dealing with a gene complex and there are other factors. Perhaps hairy men are more dominant and some females forgive the less-than-ideal hairiness to associate with a dominant male. Or many other things!

Sexual selection and the linkage disequilibrium it causes have led to bizarre effects like the elaborate displays of the birds of paradise, or the helmets and crests of the hadrosaurs. Human males have the largest penis of all the great apes though some of the apes have much larger bodies. Sexual selection with positive feedback associated with the human change to an upright posture could have been the reason. A positive feedback loop leading to explosive evolution simply requires sexual selection for a particular feature more exaggerated than the average, and the development of a linkage disequilibrium. The degree of exaggeration controls the rate of evolution with slow evolution accompanying a slight exaggeration and rapid evolution accompanying a large exaggeration.

Imagine, for the sake of illustration, how the large penis of the naked ape might have developed according to this hypothesis. Ignore cultural influences because culture, including religion and indeed clothing, had not arisen when this selection was initially taking place. The early hominids, whether by the aquatic route or the savannah route, had begun to walk upright. They had accordingly begun to adapt to copulating face-to-face. The change was not easy. Females did not find it very satisfactory in most instances because their sexual organs were still oriented rearwards. Males with longer penises could effect face-to-face intercourse more successfully.

Suppose that the average early hominid had a penis similar to a chimpanzee's but our female ancestors had more sexual satisfaction from those few males having larger penises. Males with larger penises would tend to be sexually selected, would be more successful in reproducing and would have more offspring. In time, the whole population of males would tend to have larger penises and, through linkage disequilibrium, would carry genes for the preference for larger penises among females. At the same time the females would tend to prefer males with larger penises and would carry the unexpressed genes for large penises.

What is happening is that the two sets of genes (for large penises and for the preference for large penises) are selecting each other using the size of the penis as a signal. A female chooses a male with a large penis because his large penis advertises the fact that he carries genes for the preference for a large penis. The female is choosing a male who has the same or related polygene to her own.

So, after some evolutionary time penises will be larger. The preference for large penises will also be stronger. This may even be the case though the average penis length has now become sufficient to satisfy the female when copulating in the newly adopted face-to-face position. The cycle apparently could continue locked in its positive feedback loop with ultimately bizarre consequences. In reality, of course, the feedback loop is broken and an equilibrium established when the environmental disadvantages of the feedback begin to outweigh the advantages of further response to sexual selection.

For the birds of paradise and the hadrosaurs the equilibrium was sufficiently tilted to the sexually selected side that exotic features were the result, despite their apparent disadvantages for survival. It might be interesting to know whether penises are still tending to get bigger – perhaps 30 per cent of human females still do not get adequate satisfaction from orthodox sex, suggesting that we have still not fully adapted to face-to-face copulation – but it might not be so easy to test. It is more acceptable to test tail feathers on birds.

Malte Anderson, a Swedish ethologist cut off the end of the tail feathers of some male Kenyan long-tailed widow birds. The trimmed-off ends he stuck with superglue to the ends of the tails of other birds. Thus some of the male birds had artificially long tails and some had artificially short tails. There were also controls that had had their tails cut off then stuck on again (to test whether the operation itself had any effect), and some untouched birds.

The males with the artificially long tails attracted four times as many females as the artificially short tailed birds. This proves that sexual selection is still propelling the birds towards longer tail lengths, although in practice a maximum has been reached. Longer tails render the male more liable to predation and failure to breed. But Anderson did not check whether the longer tailed birds survived less well than their short tailed rivals as the theory would predict.

So, sexual selection is one way of developing a grossly enlarged feature. Does the overdeveloped tail of a widow bird remind you of the human brain? In the sense that the human brain is another grossly overdeveloped organ and might have been produced by the effects of sexual selection, perhaps it should.

Assuming that nerve connections, the synapses, in the brain work like the elements of a computer and correspond to one of two states, on or off, then the brain, which has a hundred million million synapses, has two to the power of a hundred million million states, a number greater than the number of elementary particles in the universe. It is capable, in this computer analogy, of storing and processing immense amounts of information. Not only that, the brain also arranges its synapses into tiny microcircuits that increase still further the total number of possible states of the brain and add to the efficiency of processing information. The human brain has prodigious amounts of memory and the potential for even higher performance. Besides this huge amount of brain capacity, there is the split brain. In most animals both parts do the same things but, in humans, they have begun to specialize in various ways. We are developing two brains working in parallel on different types of problem.

Our brains have apparently overshot their optimum size. Like a computer with four megabytes of memory but which is only able to address 640 kilobytes, they have incorporated excess capacity and, at present, most of it is redundant. But sooner or later a mutation will arise that is able to make use of all that power. One need not expect subsequent evolutionary change to be slow.

Evolution often uses redundancy. Redundant parts of an organism are found new uses by evolution. Fish taking to the land no longer needed their swim-bladder, an air sac that kept the fish buoyant in the water. The swim bladder was redundant but found an excellent new use as a rudimentary lung. Higher organisms often have large amounts of apparently redundant DNA (called introns) between the coding sequences that contain the instructions for the growth of the organism. The introns contain bits of DNA with odd properties. Some are mobile, acting as though they are hitching a ride on the main sequence of the DNA molecule but cannot make up their mind where to sit. Some are "decayed" genes, no longer functional but subject to mutation. Others seem to be immune to mutation. There are repetitive sequences apparently made by bits of the code that are conceited, duplicating themselves at random places in the introns and even from one chromosome to another.

Genetic information is increased commonly by a mutation causing part of the genetic code to double. The redundant excess part is then able gradually to take on a new role. The introns seem to be one place where mutation and role adaptation can occur with ease. They are just the place to look for the causes of fast evolution of new species.

Even ordinary evolution by selection of the fittest can be extraordinarily fast. There are examples of new characteristics evolving observably such as the growth of resistance to antibiotics in bacteria, the resistance of insects to DDT and the resistance of rats and mice to warfarin rat poison. In each case resistant strains were selected in only a few generations, taking only a few years.

Every schoolchild will know of industrial melanism in the peppered moth. A rare dark variety of the moth began to outnumber the common speckled variety because of industrial pollution. Normally the speckled variety was adequately camouflaged on clean lichen-covered tree bark but pollution killed the lichen and blackened the bark making the speckled variety conspicuous. Natural selection was effected by foraging birds. The dark mutant found the blackened bark excellent camouflage and the birds missed them.

The house sparrow, introduced into North America in the middle of the 19th century has evolved into several distinct sub-species in only about 110 generations. Some plant species have separated in only 50-100 generations. Experimenters with fruit flies claim to have shown speciation to occur in only 12 generations. Lake Nabugabo became separated from Lake Victoria by a sand bar only 4000 years ago. Today the sand bar is still only three km across yet it has enabled five species of haplochromis to evolve. They are amongst the newest species we know and illustrate how quickly speciation can occur even in vertebrates when a population gets isolated.

Closely related species are nearly identical in the protein coding parts of their DNA but differ enormously in the repetitive sequences in the introns. G.A.Dover proposed that it is the differences in the apparently functionless repetitive sequences that determine the species. When these satellite sequences differ two animals cannot successfully mate. They, at best, produce sterile hybrids like the mule. The satellite sequences can change very rapidly compared with the stability of the protein coding sequences. They copy themselves rapidly to random locations, even in other chromosomes, thus providing a means of rapid speciation.

There is, in humans, a repetitive sequence amounting to three per cent of all DNA. By changing this sequence in a newly fertilized egg it might be possible to produce a different species of human being almost overnight. Though the repetitive sequences seem to be functionless, could they express themselves somehow at the macro level, perhaps in a way that could only be sensed by others with the same sequence? Could they account for forms of rapid speciation?

Are these mechanisms adequate to account for profound changes like advanced intelligence? In gradual evolution there are always countervailing factors. Can any form of gradual evolution lead to really revolutionary new physiological structures? The human brain seems to have three levels of structure, each one overlaying the previous one. What led to the adding of a new and apparently superior part to the brain on two occasions?

Some biologists have always felt that there were problems in the Darwinian view of evolution by accumulation of small changes even allowing for isolation and rapid evolution. How, for example, could it account for the major divisions in taxonomy such as that between reptiles and mammals? There seem to be too many fundamental differences between such groups of creatures. How could all these vital distinguishing features have evolved simultaneously?

One solution that has always been controversial, and still is, is saltation. Saltation is macromutation – major changes occur in a single mutation not via the accumulation of many small changes (called micromutation). The argument against saltation is that large changes in physiology caused by mutation must be harmful because they amount to a gross deformity. The chances that a deformity on this scale would be beneficial to a creature are considered to be vanishingly small.

R.A.Fisher used the analogy of a microscope to show that macromutations cannot lead to viable changes. Imagine a microscope almost in focus. The focus is the evolutionary equilibrium state and the microscope is nearly at it. Suppose a tiny small random movement of the microscope adjustment were made to represent a micromutational change. The microscope barrel can only move inwards or outwards so there is a 50 per cent probability that the change will improve the focussing and a 50 per cent probability that it will make it worse. Eventually, through accumulating such small mutations, the microscope could become fully focussed.

What though if the random change to the adjustment were large? Moving the barrel in the wrong direction would obviously worsen the focus; but moving in the correct direction would also worsen the focus, because a macromutation, a large change, would considerably overshoot it. A random mutation could be in the right direction and exactly the size needed to drop the microscope into focus, but this is so unlikely compared with all the other possibilities that it can be safely ignored. In practice a random large change cannot improve the focus of the instrument.

The alert reader will notice that this analogy is a terrible example of evolution. Evolution is not random in its overall effect precisely because natural selection tends to eliminate the bad variations. The microscope would tend to become focussed because the micromutations away from the focus would die out leaving those that were tending towards the focus. The macromutations would die out anyway because they must always be further from the focus.

What, now, if this microscope had two foci? If, for example, it had two eyepieces which were themselves not equally adjusted so that when one was in focus, the other was not, and vice versa. Now there are two chances of getting a focus, one with each eye. If the microscope were adjusted close to one focus, the micromutational argument of Fisher would still apply, but what of the macromutational argument. There must be a chance that a random macromutation would put the other eyepiece into better focus than it was – perhaps, even put it into better focus than the instrument had before. In this case a macromutation could improve the overall focus of the instrument. Though it is still unlikely, it is more likely than before.

How does this translate into arguments about evolution? In the analogy of a multidimensional evolutionary space, a hyperspace, stable forms correspond to depressions in the landscape. The flow of evolution can be imagined as the flow of a river down the valleys of this landscape into a depression, forming a lake corresponding to a stable species or a developed feature. Translating the microscope analogy into the landscape analogy, we find a lake at the microscope focus, the species equilibrium position, but on either side of it we are moving uphill away from the focus. The uplands are bleak. Individuals here are badly adapted, the result of mutation: species here are badly adapted, the result of a changed environment. Finding themselves there they had better quickly head downhill towards the lake (the focus of the microscope in Fisher's analogy) by evolving rapidly or die. Death is, of course, extinction for the species or the effect of a disastrous mutation on an individual.

The microscope with two foci is a landscape with two valleys separated by a hill. A macromutation, a large jump from the edge of the lake in one valley could land you in, or close to, the lake in the other valley. If the other valley were deeper and steeper (representing a highly specialized species), merely landing on the other side of the watershed might lead to rapid evolution to the new species – the flow down the steep hillside would be rapid. The mutants, though ill-adapted, must become rapidly fitter by micromutational (Darwinian) selection or perish anyway. Far from macromutation being always unsuccessful in a multidimensional space, there are rare occasions when it is successful and provides the sudden jump that the fossil record needs to explain the distinctions between major groups of organisms like families.

Richard Dawkins argues that "virtually all the mutations studied in genetics laboratories – which are pretty macro because otherwise geneticists wouldn't notice them – are deleterious to the animals possessing them". Since he says "virtually all", the implication is that some macro mutations studied in the laboratory are beneficial, or at least neutral, to the animal possessing them. Even if the "virtually" were erased, one is entitled to ask how an evolutionist could imagine that, however many experiments were carried out in laboratories, the vastness of the range of nature's experiments could be reproduced. Even accelerated evolution usually depends upon passages of many millennia, impossible to simulate in a laboratory. This is especially true of saltation precisely because beneficial macromutations are, as all agree, rare.

But Dawkins readily accepts that the type of mutation he refers to as "the stretched DC8 macromutation" is not unusually rare. Like the DC8 aeroplane lengthened by adding a new section of hull, mutations of this sort would put a complete additional segment into a millipede, extra ribs into a snake or an extra digit to a human hand. According to Dawkins these are really micromutations. Although they are major changes for the complete organism, they are only small changes to the genetic instructions. If you were to write a computer program to print five asterisks in a row you could write a program to print one asterisk then put the program into a loop telling the computer to repeat the instruction five times. If you found that six asterisks had actually appeared you would not think that the complete set of instructions to print another asterisk had miraculously been duplicated. You would realize there was one small error – you had mistyped six for five in your program which had then looped six times not five.

Dawkins says that disposes of saltation – when it occurs it is not a macromutation at all. But it actually justifies it. It makes macromutation at the whole organism level more likely, depending as it does on only a micromutation at the level of the program, the genetic code. Small changes in genes that are subtly linked together to influence a complex of apparently unrelated features can have profound changes on the organism. The environment effects natural selection on the whole organism not on the genes themselves, so it is the macro effects that matter in the selection process.

Some micromutations can simply be the re-expression of a previously unexpressed gene or group of genes. The interesting aspect of this effect is that it can cause apparent violations of Dollo's Law in that features which have apparently disappeared can reappear. When a macro feature is lost during evolution it does not follow that its genetic blueprint has gone, simply that it has switched off. The complete genetic blueprint is never fully expressed in advanced animals. The inoperative bit of genetic code will be lost eventually.

Mutation will lead to reprogramming of the redundant piece, although that might be millions of years later. A feature which has disappeared has done so for a reason. It is unlikely that conditions would turn again in its favor before the underlying code had been altered – thus upholding Dollo's Law. But, though usually so, it need not always be true and lost features can reappear, albeit rarely. If the section of genetic code remains intact, it can occasionally be expressed by accident causing atavisms or throwbacks. If the throwback happened to be again of value to the organism, it could again be selected.

Atavisms, as one would expect, mainly look bizarre and are not of any benefit – quite the opposite. Three toed horses are not particularly uncommon, the extra toes not being a crippling deformity, but whales with rear limbs are more unusual. Both represent throwbacks of tens of millions of years of evolution. No birds today have teeth but experiments have shown that birds are capable of growing them given the right conditions. Surgical manipulation in a chicken's foetus can induce structures to grow that normally would not. The genetic instructions for their growth must be present even though they are not usually expressed. Furthermore, the growth of some structures induces the growth of others. The fibula in a chicken normally has atrophied to a splinter. Yet if it is encouraged to grow until it reaches the ankle, lo and behold, ankle bones, that normally do not grow at all in a chicken, appear.

The hoatzin chick is, in some respects, a throwback to the archaeopteryx. It has the three grasping claws on its forelimbs seen in the archaeopteryx but not present in other birds including the hoatzin's near relatives. They recede in the adult form. Evolution seems to have partly revived an otherwise discarded plan by bringing it out of genetic storage because for one odd bird it has proved advantageous. The hoatzin chick can cling to reeds, roots and branches above the marshes where it lives.

The apparent loss of the wishbone or collar bones in dinosaurs seemed to preclude them as ancestors of the birds. Consequently Heilmann in 1925 proposed that primitive reptiles called pseudosuchians were the ancestors of both birds and dinosaurs. Birds retained the wishbone but dinosaurs, in the main, lost it. What renders this theory untenable is that the archaeopteryx with its wishbone is so uncannily like some dinosaurs without it. Possibly some of the bird branch and some of the dinosaur branch evolved in parallel, having split from the pseudosuchians. But the anatomy of archaeopteryx and its dinosaur twins is so close except for the wishbone that convergence seems less likely than that the collar bone reappeared as a throwback in species that had lost it. If atavism is caused by failed suppressor genes then even though dinosaurs like deinonychus had lost their wishbones, the genetic information for wishbone production still existed and could be recalled. In archaeopteryx, it proved advantageous to do so. Powerful flight muscles anchored to the revived wishbones were essential to flight and the evolution of birds.

Having found itself with a new, or revived, macro-feature, the mutant organism, whether it be bird or bacterium, finds itself in a new evolutionary channel possibly leading to an undiscovered Shangri-La in the evolutionary landscape. With its novel characteristics, the mutant can evolve rapidly and, ultimately, disperse into the niches available to it.

In the evolutionary landscape lakes are stasis and torrents tumbling down steep hillsides are rapid evolution. Both are understandable in the ways outlined above, so, long periods of little change and short periods of rapid change can be explained provided that the conditions are suitable for each. But could evolution be yet more highly directed? Could the development of the embryo be an initial mutational filter, a preselector especially valuable in selecting viable saltational changes?

Embryos spontaneously abort if a macromutation is unsuitable for embryological development. Subject to micromutations only, the embryo will survive until birth because small changes will not normally affect its viability. But macromutations very often are not viable for survival of the embryo. The windpipe might be missing or the heart punctured. The brain might be large but the neck too weak to support it, and so on. Development of the embryo is a filter for macromutations. Rejects are spontaneously aborted stopping the parent from wasting time and effort on unviable offspring. Hence the only macromutations that see the light of day are those that permit survival of the embryo until birth. Many, if not most, of those will also die, but successful embryological development is the first stage of natural selection.

Evolution might be a vector quantity, having direction as well as magnitude. A species in stasis and subject to no particular selection pressure experiences mutations in all directions in evolutionary space and most are neutral or selected against. But once evolution towards a new equilibrium position begins to occur, mutations in one direction can be favored by selection – evolution can therefore be a vector quantity in evolutionary space complete with its own momentum.

Not all genetic mutations are equally likely. Mutation can be itself controlled to some extent by a gene. That is not to say that all mutations are thus controlled, random mutations will still occur, but a gene could tag another gene or mixture of genes for change when appropriate. Such a gene could control the extent to which a group of genes mutate thus effectively providing a mechanism for macromutation in the right conditions. It is a gene having mutagenic properties leading to saltation, a saltatory gene, a saltagen. In stable conditions the saltagen, which itself mutates readily, would be switched off. Obviously it would have no effect on evolution. If it switched on, since the species is in stasis, the mutations would tend to be unfavorable and selected against. If conditions changed, and the saltagen switched on some mutations would be favored and selected. The saltatory quantum would be one, one gene at a time would mutate, it would be in its x1 quantum state. In a subsequent generation it could mutate to the x2 state, triggering other genes to mutate or single genes to mutate more. In the offspring of those which survive, the saltagen would mutate again, perhaps to a x4 state, inducing more mutations in the main sequence genes which it influences. Further mutations to x8 etc could occur as long as the gene was transmitted to a successful later generation.

What are the conditions for activation of the saltagen? The environment must have changed sharply (in geological terms) so that the species is unstable in it. It is ill-fitted to the conditions in some way. The saltatory gene determines how much mutation occurs in the genes which it controls. As long as the next generation survives, the saltagens it carries will also survive and be able to switch to higher states. Each higher state will cause larger amounts of genetic change. Eventually it will cause macromutation of the organism.

Obviously a stage will be reached when the saltagen's mutational steps and the scale of genetic change are so large that the mutations induced are all damaging. Selection or embryonic preselection will then tend to eliminate the individuals with the highest level of saltagen and the escalating process will go into reverse eventually switching off the saltatory gene when stasis is again reached. The gene then only switches on randomly, to test the environment, so to speak. This process allows a faster approach towards the evolutionary solution. It also might go some way towards accommodating the "creative evolution" of Bergson and Shaw, generally frowned upon by orthodox evolutionists.

"All very fanciful," I hear sceptics say, "but where is the evidence?" Professor John Fincham of Edinburgh University, Scotland writes, "the spontaneous mutation frequency of an organism is to a large extent controlled by its own genotype." In other words organisms mutate at rates controlled by their own genes. Precisely. The saltagen controls the mutational rate.

We know organisms have genes called antimutator genes which provide mechanisms to repair DNA chains that have replicated wrongly. These DNA repair and mutation avoidance mechanisms work thus: the faulty bit of DNA is tagged by some suitable chemical sidechain, specific chemicals called enzymes seek out the tag, cut out the faulty part and replace it with the correct piece. A gene observed in the gut bacterium, E. coli, is called Treffers Gene. Normally it acts as an antimutator gene, but it too is subject to mutation. When it mutates its effectiveness in suppressing mutations in other genes decreases, making the rate of mutation of these genes rise a hundred times. Here we have a gene which, when mutated causes other genes to mutate more. A saltagen?

Another mechanism operates while the DNA chain is replicating. DNA polymerase, an enzyme that has the function of building the DNA polymer, checks the chain as it is being built. It "proof reads" each copy of the genetic code. If the last monomer it added matches the DNA template, the unraveled DNA strand from the previous generation, then a new monomer is added. If it does not match, the DNA polymerase cuts the previous monomer away and replaces it with a correct one. But certain mutations affect the DNA polymerase itself, rendering it not such a good "proof reader." The result? More mutations of the genes during their construction!

Many DNA sequences have more than one function. They can be read more than once with different results. My milkman sees a message by my doorstep saying, "No milk today" with a pointer that can be directed at the word "No" or the word "milk." If it points to the "No," I get no milk but if it points to the milk," I get milk. The code "No milk today" does not alter but the outcome depends on where the message starts. That illustrates one way that one stretch of DNA can be read differently. Another way would be to read it in a different order, akin to reading the word STAR (forwards) or RATS (backwards). The way in which the bit of code is read is determined by a previous bit of code. Errors in these instructions can have profound effects on the meaning of a genetic sequence and thence on the macro features of an organism. An example is the pseudogene for production of globin, a protein, in humans.

Pseudogenes are "decayed" genes. The pseudogene for globin is all but identical to active genes for globin production but have mutated in their initiation codon, the piece of DNA coding sequence saying where the message starts, and also in other parts of the code. In short, the mechanism for reading the gene no longer operates. It seems a piece of DNA containing the active globin gene mutated by doubling then one of the bits fell out of use, remaining only as redundant code.

What causes plagues? I am not digressing. The answer provides an interesting example of the effect of a copying error and switching off a gene. Hans Wolf-Watz of the University of Umea in Sweden and his team have looked at the DNA sequences of the plague bacterium, Yersinia. Normally this bacterium is not very virulent, but occasionally a copying error occurs in which one letter of the code is lost thus scrambling a whole coding sequence. The function of that part of the code is not known but the effect of the error gives a clue – the mutant bacterium is deadly. The piece of code helps the host to defend itself against the bacterium. Why should it do that? Simply because by not doing, it kills off its hosts rapidly leaving it with nowhere to live – it too dies. With the bit of protective code active the host is likely to survive and the bacterium with it. The protective sequence is in a part of the code that has a high mutation rate so deadly mutants are thrown up quite often, but plague epidemics are not very frequent. The reason is that the virulent form of Yersinia normally kills its host before it has had time to be transmitted to another. Only in overcrowded and unsanitary conditions is it able to spread from one host to another before the hapless host is done in.

The rapidly mutating piece of code looks as though it switches on occasionally to test the environment. If it is suitable – conditions are overcrowded and unsanitary – the virulent bacterium spreads rapidly but otherwise it dies out for awhile until reborn by a replicating error. A gene which switches on to test the environment – just like a saltagen!

Even more relevant may be a phenomenon called "replicating instability" which, unlike the examples just mentioned, seems to be a positive effect rather than a negative one, although it is not yet understood. It seems to allow a "propensity to mutate" to transmit through an indefinite number of replications before, for some reason, it manifests itself. Isn't that another gene that is switched off until the conditions are right?

Earlier we speculated about an incest gene. If there were such a thing it could, once it had turned on, remain switched on so that it actually provided the distinguishing feature of the new species. Linked to some physical characteristic it would be recognizable by all others possessing the gene, drawing them inexorably into mutual reproduction. As more creatures were born with the gene, it would cease to cause incest because others not in the immediate family would also carry the gene. It will have become a breeding preference distinguishing two populations and eventually leading to speciation. Alternatively, perhaps like the saltagen, it turns on under environmental pressure for change – in other words when there is a need for rapid evolution. This could have been true of certain apes in the last ten million years or so, judging by the successive waves of hominids appearing until the Cro-Magnon variety, only a few tens of thousands of years ago. Either way it can permit speciation when it might not be expected and therefore speed up evolution. Jane van Lawick Goodall has noted that chimpanzees and other primates show no sexual interest in their mothers. Yet men seem obsessed by the Oedipal complex. That man carries the incest gene unlike his primate cousins might be the key distinction between them. Have we evolved rapidly because we are the Oedipal ape?

"Impressive testimony to the existence of a fast-acting mechanism" for creating extra bits of DNA sequence, according to Fincham, is the behavior of cells cultivated in the drug methotrexate. An excess of this drug, which inhibits one of the cell's enzymes, in the environment causes the cells to develop enormously lengthened chromosomes carrying multiple repeats of the DNA segment for production of the enzyme. In response to the intense selection pressure of the harmful drug, the cell repeatedly mutated by doubling the satellite sequence containing the code it needed to manufacture the enzyme under attack. This is hardly random mutation. "Impressive testimony" indeed.

Fincham sums up thus: "These mechanisms are themselves subject to mutation and natural selection and the spontaneous mutation frequencies which we find in natural populations of organisms of all kinds are adaptive. They presumably represent a compromise between short-term need to replicate already well adapted DNA sequences with sufficient precision and the longer term advantage of variability."

The mutation rate per gene is only one per million replications but, because a lot of genes are needed to define an organism, that makes mutation quite likely in the whole DNA sequence. Large organisms average about one mutation in ten replications many of which, we have noted, are harmful and most of those that are not are neutral. This may be near the acceptable limit for human DNA. More complex DNA would mutate too often making reproduction unreliable. Hence beyond this level of complexity, evolution favors the storage of information in the brain rather than in the genes.

By comparing the amount of information estimated to be in the genes of different types of animal with the amount of information estimated to be in their brains, Carl Sagan deduces that "somewhere in the steamy jungles of the Carboniferous Period" animals emerged with more information in their brains than in their genes. This estimate is quite imperfect because the information is imprecise and the figures cover a large range requiring logarithmic relationships which exaggerate errors. But, though the date of the crossover is inexact, the notion seems valid. Since the crossover point, whenever it was, brains have increasingly dominated genes. This suggests there might be a threshold beyond which evolutionary pressure builds up to develop brain rather than extend the complexity of the DNA. Some dinosaurs, having passed the threshold, might have built up an evolutionary head of steam for intelligence.

Evolution is faster for birds and mammals than for the cold blooded amphibians, fish and reptiles. At the annual meeting of the British Association for the Advancement of Science in 1988 Allan Wilson, of the University of California at Berkeley, proposed that animals with larger EQs evolve faster than less brainy relatives. Wilson believes the increase in brain size accounts for their difference in evolutionary speeds. If true then one can expect an explosive evolution of the brain by positive feedback.

To measure evolutionary differences, Wilson took 20,000 bone measurements from 400 species of vertebrates. From these results he created an index of how different the shape of the body was for any two vertebrate species. Closely related species like the coal tit and the blue tit had an index of 3 whereas the differences between an eagle and a sparrow were reflected in their index of 25. Combining this index with the date of separation of species using the molecular clock allowed Wilson to plot evolutionary change against time. He found that evolution is speeding up.

His explanation is that brains drive evolution: "as brains became bigger and bigger they became the predominant cause of the pressure to evolve." More intelligent species are more willing to try new forms of behavior and that gives more scope for selection to operate. When a group of animals have learnt a new behavior then evolution will change their physical attributes the better to take advantage of the new behavior. Animals evolve more quickly when their brains are advanced enough to allow them to modify their behavior. The creature's body then evolves along the lines best suited to the new behavior pattern. Because the brain is both one of the physical attributes subject to evolution and a factor controlling the rate of that evolution, a chain reaction occurs by positive feedback. The result is exponential growth – growth which is at an ever increasing rate.

Wilson believes that innovation and imitation among our hominid ancestors provided selective pressure for physical changes including greater brain size. "Those lineages with larger brains evolve more and more quickly, and eventually you get a species which is so intelligent that cultural evolution takes over entirely from genetic evolution." Our ape-like ancestors of the past few million years "have undergone one of the fastest rates of evolution on record. The brain almost trebled in size, the larynx, tongue and lips changed as speech developed, the thumb and fingers altered so that we could manipulate tools with precision, and walking on two legs was perfected," relates science writer, Nicholas Schoon.

According to Wilson, it is inevitable that overwhelmingly intelligent species should dominate the planet. If humans were to die out another mammal or a bird, would replace us. Since exponential growth is steady continuous growth but at an ever increasing rate, for a very long period both size and growth rate are so small that changes can hardly be noticed, but eventually the growth rate seems to take off, as if it had passed a threshold. This is just what we see in the growth of intelligence. It is as if, in our evolutionary hyperspace, intelligence is a lake at the bottom of a trough with steeper slopes the closer the approach to the surface of the lake. You slip down the slope gathering momentum until you tumble over the edge. Any creature getting to the edge will find itself precipitated into the Sea of Knowledge.

There are conflicting views about how easily intelligence evolves. Some say it is rare yet I argue that species are accelerating towards ever higher intelligence. The conflict is explained by the hazards of getting to where the slope starts perceptibly to incline towards the sea of knowledge. There are many other comfortable troughs that species can settle in before it gets to the edge, just as a golfer might find it difficult to get on to the green without getting trapped in a bunker – and this is not a par five hole: it has countless dog legs and bunkers on the way. The many species that have existed on earth without developing intelligence couldn't get out of the bunkers. So far, not many have got to the green, the equivalent in the golfing analogy to the sea of our landscape analogy.

What is clear is that, given certain attributes, intelligence seems bound to evolve – and quickly. Some dinosaurs seem to have had those attributes and could have developed rapidly, just as we have.

CHAPTER NINE

ANTHROPOSAURUS SAPIENS

"The greatest intelligence is precisely the one that suffers most from its own limitations."

Andre Gide

Did the dinosaurs develop intelligence before Adam? Some dinosaur iconoclasts have dared to ask this question, but even they have merely answered: "They couldn't have". Thus Bakker asks: "Why didn't [the dinosaurs] evolve larger cerebral systems? Why didn't they eventually produce super-intelligent species capable of making stone tools?" Desmond compares mammals with the superior dinosaurs and wonders: "Why did not "Man" land on the moon in the Cretaceous?" adding that by "Man" he meant a creature filling the ecological role of humans. Sagan asks "if the dinosaurs had not all been mysteriously extinguished some sixty-five million years ago, would the saurornithoides have continued to evolve into increasingly intelligent forms?" All believe dinosaurs would have reached intelligence were it not for the Cretaceous terminal extinction. And all agree that they failed to achieve it because they died out first.

I disagree. Some dinosaurs did develop intelligence and by so doing caused the Cretaceous terminal extinction, just as an insensitive ape developed intelligence at the end of the Tertiary and created the mass extinction that marks the end of that geological era. Though the direct evidence is sparse – I give what little there is in the next chapter – the circumstantial evidence is compelling. The thesis is not self-evidently false, as, say, the idea of a flat earth is. Today we consider it evident that the earth is round and revolves round the Sun – but these ideas have only become accepted in the last few hundred years. The movement of the continents, continental drift, noted by Wegener sixty years ago seems obvious to us all now, indeed it was probably obvious to any child studying a map of the world decades before Wegener, but because continents were so massive and the experts could not think of a mechanism by which they could move, no one was willing to ask the question "must not South America and Africa once have been joined?" We might find ourselves realizing simultaneously that the anthroposaur preceded us, and that we have just stumbled over the precipice of our own extinction.

Mankind has adopted its position of global domination in just five million years. The dinosaurs, we have seen, were warm-blooded, active creatures and usurped the rule of the thecodonts in only five million years. Mechanisms exist for species to evolve at astonishingly fast rates. On average a species of dinosaur did not last for more than two or three million years before becoming extinct or evolving into a new species. There is no reason why one of the dinosaurs should not have evolved intelligence during the last five million years or so of the Cretaceous Period. Dinosaurs evolved quickly and there was a spate of dinosaur evolution just prior to their final decline. Bakker says that the stenonychosaurs were "evolving quickly in many of their adaptive compartments" and with their bulky pair of mid-brain lobes they were probably "every bit as endowed as the Late Cretaceous mammals".

Fossil dinosaurs have been found with quite remarkably large brains... for dinosaurs. One authority says that triceratops had a brain weighing a kilogram, a fair size compared with our 1.5 kilograms, though its body weight was 9000 kg compared with our 70 kg. Struthiomimus had a brain to body ratio similar to that of a modern day ostrich – 1:1000. And, though brain size is obviously a general measure of intelligence, there is no way of telling whether the brain of an extinct class of animals functioned in quite the same way as those of animals with which we are familiar. We cannot be certain that modern creatures with larger brains are more intelligent than the smaller brained dinosaurs. A higher metabolic rate, more active brains, faster synapses, sharper nerve impulses could all contribute to greater efficiency of the brain even though it were smaller than ours. Of course, size is presumably directly related to memory capacity but, for humans, much of the brain seems redundant, evolution looks to have overshot – a result, perhaps, of sexual selection or a saltagen in a high quantum state. It might not have done for dinosaurs whose memory capacity could have been better adjusted to the capabilities of their brains overall.

Then again the nature of their intelligence might have differed from ours. Many cold-blooded animals do very well in the world of the mammals by using abilities other than intelligence. In South America, farmers use marine toads to suppress mice and rats which otherwise would make a feast of their crops and seeds. A ponderous toad successfully preying on wily rats? Yet they do. The toads, weighing five pounds wait with infinite patience for the cleverer victim to traverse its usual path, it pounces and the rat is gulped whole into the frog's maw, rendered insensible by poisonous saliva then swallowed. The abilities of dinosaurs might also have developed rather differently from mammals. But even if dinosaur and mammalian evolution were truly parallel and dinosaurs had to evolve big brains to become intelligent, fast evolution could have done it in a relatively short time.

You do not have to believe me. Witness this remarkable paragraph by Adrian Desmond: "the most intriguing Late Cretaceous inhabitants were the intelligent mimics unearthed in recent years – wide eyed ostrich dinosaurs, and dromaeosaurids like deinonychus and the saurornithoides with stereo-vision functionally mated to opposable thumbs. These dinosaurs, capable of more skilful behavioral feats than any other land animal hitherto, were separated from other dinosaurs by a gulf comparable to that dividing men from cows: the disparity in brain size is staggering. The potential in dromaeosaurs and coelurosaurs for an explosive evolution as the Tertiary dawned cannot be doubted – who knows what new peaks the sophisticated 'bird-mimics' would have attained had they survived into the 'Age of Mammals'. Yet apparently not a breeding population of these beautiful, alert dinosaurs outlived the comparatively cumbersome and dim-witted giants".

Desmond almost proposes that the dinosaurs became intelligent but he pulls up at the final hurdle. Yes the "explosive evolution" did occur. Mankind has evolved from being a user of crude rock tools to our present level of civilization in just one million years. It must be possible that these alert creatures did the same. How would that have looked in the fossil record, especially bearing in mind that the chosen habitat of these dinosaurs made their remains scarce, just as remains of early man are scarce and, of modern chimpanzees, non-existent?

Dale Russell, discoverer of stenonychosaurus, has also postulated that late Cretaceous dinosaurs were well on the way to becoming intellectual animals, and would have succeeded if the dinosaurs had not suffered extinction, stenonychosaurus had an opposable thumb, stood upright about three feet tall and had binocular vision. Russell commented, "it had all the ingredients of success that we see later in the development of the apes." He believes that stenonychosaurs were the "chief predators on Cretaceous mammals" and that there must have been quite a lot of them because, by the end of the Cretaceous, there were a lot of mammals, though they were small. Nevertheless few have been found as fossils, just as complete fossil mammals from that period are also rare. "The fossil record is so limited that it is a pitiful reflection of past life", as Norman Myers puts it.

Russell deduced the appearance of a stenonychosaurus that had evolved unhampered by disasters until the 20th century. A model of the creature, a dinosauroid, is on display in Ottawa. The conception of the dinosauroid was based upon convergent evolution. Russell extrapolated trends observable in the dinosaurs like stenonychosaurus to beyond their extinction. By the 20th century, Russell believes their brain size would have been within the human range. To accommodate it its skull would have expanded and its face would probably have flattened. The long dinosaur neck would have shortened to bear more comfortably the weight of its brain. Consequently its tail would have been lost since it would not have been needed to counterpoise the neck and head. He assumed live births and, rather illogically, that the dinosauroid would therefore have needed a navel. The young, though, were thought likely to have been fed on regurgitated food and the creature would not have had any "mammalia". Communication would have sounded similar to birdsong.

Besides these conjectured features he supposes there would be characteristics typical of dinosaurs such as scaly skin, large oval eyes with vertically slit pupils, absence of external sex organs and a three fingered hand, one digit of which would be opposed. "Absence of external sex organs" – possibly, but, although the tuatara lizard of New Zealand which is very similar to lizards from 200 million years ago has no penis, the marine iguanas of the Galapagos islands have them. Most reptiles and birds procreate by pushing together their cloacae which are openings in the body doubling up as a sexual tract and an anus. This seems a bit of a hit and miss affair to the intelligent mammal and, if Bakker's arguments are to mean anything, one would have thought that hot-blooded, sexually active dinosaurs would have evolved a more certain method of procreation. However, if birds are examples of latter day dinosaurs, Russell could be correct, and birds don't seem to have any trouble in procreating. Nevertheless, if convergent evolution had required a convergence of shape appropriate for a thinking creature, the upright stance of the human and the ventro-ventral mode of copulation it induces, might have dictated the evolution of a penis in the dinosauroid, if not in other dinosaurs.

We considered some possibility of major differences in the structure of the brain of the dinosauroid and man. In mammals the brain grew by expansion of the cerebral lobes but in birds it was the corpus striatum that expanded. A great deal of visual information processing in reptiles is done in the retina rather than being passed on to the brain. The ostrich mimic dinosaur had enormous eyes protected by bony plates. That is usually attributed to a nocturnal lifestyle but it could indicate that the parts of the brain of the dinosauroid that were to develop were associated with vision.

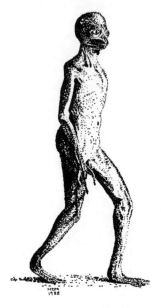

Exhibit 6. Dale Russell's dinosauroid

Russell was almost at pains to emphasize that his guesses were conservative – and that must be true. 65 million years, even in a thought experiment, seems too long for an active, warm-blooded creature already up and running to need to develop what mammals did in the same period of time from a standing start. With the mechanisms for rapid change at the disposal of evolution such a long time scale seems unnecessary if not silly. It is more likely that intelligence evolved before the whole dinosaurian dynasty came to an end. Russell's conjectures give us a model, not of the impossible but of the possible. Not of the hypothetical dinosauroid today but the actual anthroposaur of 65 million years ago.

Within a few million years of the extinction of the dinosaurs, the neocortex of the early primates had begun to develop. Quite ordinary mammals now exhibit astonishingly sophisticated behavior that denotes the working of sophisticated brains. Consider three quick examples. Compared with the hoofed animals of the veldt, hyenas are slow creatures. They can run at about 40 mph compared with 50 mph for a wildebeest. They have therefore learned to be clever team hunters. Often lions scavenge from hyenas rather than the other way around. The hyaena seems to decide upon the type of prey it wants in advance then uses appropriate tactics for that creature. David Attenborough tells us that they are happy to hunt wildebeest but will ignore them if they have decided that today's dinner is to be zebra. Prairie dogs, communal animals that live in "towns" go in for horticulture. They cut down certain plants, not to eat – they do not like the taste of them – but to create more space for those they do like. Every now and then they leave a territory for no other reason than to let it lie fallow to recover, then they return to it. Finally Sea otters are intelligent enough to use a tool, such as a suitable pebble, to break shellfish from the rocks and to crack open their shells.

All evolved since the death of the dinosaurs. Yet surely the selective pressure on the mammals in the world of the dinosaurs would have been more favorable to the development of the mammalian neocortex. Intelligence is a weapon in the evolutionary arms race between predator and prey. The mammals were the oppressed animals, oppressed by the superior dinosaurs. Plainly, if the mammals were more intelligent than the dinosaurs then they should have been able to outwit them and usurp the dinosaur's dominant status. They didn't so they weren't. The mammals, including the primates, could not capitalize on intelligence in the Cretaceous because there already were intelligent creatures around quite capable of holding their own against other dinosaurs let alone the pretensions of early primates or any other mammal. Just as mankind eliminated the intelligent opposition, the anthroposaurs would have eliminated any other animal, dinosaur or mammal, that seemed likely to become a rival.

What of the niche later occupied by the primates. Was it occupied in the Cretaceous by primosaurs, dinosaur equivalents of the primates, and only when they died was the mammalian version able to develop? If convergent evolution is anything to go by, perhaps the intelligent dinosaur had to descend, like the intelligent mammal, from the trees or, perhaps, emerge from the water. What was in the trees when the dinosaurs were on the ground? From the fossil record there seem to be no dinosaurs adapted for tree dwelling in the sense that such creatures as monkeys, apes or even squirrels are today. Yet, if there were no dinosaurs in the trees, the mammals would have had a perfectly safe niche, would surely have evolved into it and, if they merely had to find a place free of dinosaurs to realize their destiny, developed brains much earlier.

Fossils of predatory dinosaurs are rare – Robert Bakker claims that he only came across a few fragments of them in six years of field work – but fossils of forest species are rarer. Fossil chimpanzees, from much closer times, are totally non-existent. We have only five fossil skeletons of Archaeopteryx which presumably spent some of its time in trees. Fossils of pterosaurs are mainly of marine species which swooped around the edges of the sea. The problem with tree dwellers is that their dead bodies drop to the forest floor where they are most unlikely to leave a fossil record. The forest is rich in fungi and bacteria that thrive in the damp and the shade and the little that is not eaten by scavengers decays in a short time. And the bones? – the forest floor is acidic so that even the bones do not survive long enough to leave a trace.

So there is no fossil evidence to suggest what was in the trees when dinosaurs roamed the ground. Experts tell us that, since mammals, like tree shrews, were there, dinosaurs were not – otherwise trees would not have been safe for them. But, if the dinosaurs were afraid of heights, how did the pterosaurs and archaeopteryx learn to fly? It is absurd that dinosaurs should not have adapted to life in the trees and the pterosaurs and archaeopteryx prove it. Lagosuchus, thought to be an ancestor of the pterodactyls, was a primitive dinosaur that must have climbed trees. Today, Komodo dragon hatchlings live in trees to avoid predators. Many other cold-blooded animals climb trees, the many species of tree frog for instance. Why should there not have been hosts of dinosaur monkeys and dinosaur apes? Perhaps there were but, as we have seen, because of their habitat they did not fossilize easily: a whole fauna of advanced dinosaurs about which we know nothing. Is it so stupid then to guess that one of them might have followed a pathway to intelligence just as we did?

There is a parallel between the explosive radiation of dinosaurian grazers like hadrosaurs and ceratopsians from the middle Cretaceous and the explosion of mammalian grazers about 11 million years ago. The mid-Cretaceous explosion was a result of the breakthrough of the flowering plants about 117 million years ago just as the more recent case was due to the emergence of the grasses 24 million years ago. Along with the antelopes, horses, cows and elephants of the latter period, taking advantage of the new food stuff, came the intelligent mammal, man. Lucy walked by that East African lakeside just as cattle and horses were evolving 3.7 million years ago. Since then, man has continued to evolve rapidly, though the animals that originally shared the savannah with him, such as the antelopes, have not.

Can the parallel be extended? Did an intelligent dinosaur emerge from the Cretaceous forests, a part of the explosive radiation of dinosaurs resulting from the earlier emergence of the flowering plants as a new source of food, and, like man, evolve exceedingly rapidly? If an aquatic phase gave man many useful features during his development, is it possible that some dinosaurs lived aquatically for awhile and developed a comparable streamlined shape and upright stance as well as other useful features?

With the plucking of the hadrosaurs from the experts' approved place in the swamps, to be placed in herds on mossy plains, there seemed to be no semi-aquatic dinosaurs remaining at the end of the Cretaceous. Animals such as the ichthyosaurs and the plesiosaurs, which the experts do not classify as dinosaurs, were fully aquatic, and the ichthyosaurs might have died out before then anyway. Yet, for 20 million years, sea-levels had been higher than at any time in the last 200 million years. There were vast areas of shallow continental seas. Surely a lot of species must have dipped their toes in the water and some of them must have tarried awhile. Lots of shallow seas imply lots of small, perhaps transient, islands ideal for evolutionary experiments like those described by Elaine Morgan – but 65 million years earlier. Suggestive also is Bakker's idea that the archaeopteryx was possibly able to use its primitive wings to swim rather as a hoatzin fledgling does. Both archaeopteryx and deinonychus had wrists with a semicircular joint which permitted accurate movement of the fingers and exceptional ability to flex them. It is conceivable that, while the archaeopteryx was evolving into birds that some other members of the family turned to brachiating and developed along the lines of first the modern primates, and then the aquatic ape, to yield Anthroposaurus sapiens.

Gribbon and Cherfas attribute the growth of intelligence in man to the succession of ice ages over the last few million years. This sequence of glacials and interglacials subjected the hominid apes to repeated intense selective pressure putting a premium on adaptability, versatility and intelligence. Though there were no ice ages at the end of the Cretaceous period, we noted that the sea level was high. It fell considerably and quickly 95 million years ago and again 67 million years ago, but over several million years, about 80 million years ago, there was a shallower dip. With large amounts of the continental shelves covered in water, fluctuations of only a few meters could successively expose then inundate large areas of land. The normal tidal range today can make the sea disappear over the horizon at low tide in those places where the beach shelves at only a slight angle. The slow shallow dip observed in the sea level when it was at its height possibly signifies thousands of such incursions of the ocean. Imagine a Spring tide that went out for ten thousand years before it returned. Then it stayed in for ten thousand years. This would put strong selection pressure on the species living on the flat coastal lowlands or on low islands.

Possible confirmation is the formation of oil bearing rocks at that time. Half of our present oil reserves stem from that period, the result of organic matter settling to the bottom of shallow stagnant seas. Incursions of the ocean would have trapped the organic layers between thin layers of mud eventually giving rise to oil shales from which oil was squeezed under pressure. Further evidence of such cycles comes from the striated appearance of Cretaceous chalk cliffs. Is it possible that fluctuations in sea level provided the evolutionary stimulus for the anthroposaurs that Gribbon and Cherfas argue was provided by ice ages in the evolution of mankind? Did the same fluctuations force a brachiating dromaeosaur to turn to the water temporarily, giving it a range of advantages just as Morgan argues for mankind's predecessor?

"A final mystery looms large in the story of [dinosaur] predator and prey", Robert Bakker tells us. It is that, unlike the ankylosaurs and the ceratopsians, the hadrosaurs had no obvious means of defence against ferocious predators like the tyrannosaurs. They "had no whiplike tails, long claws, or any type of spike or plate. And their limbs were shorter and designed for lower top speeds than were those of their gracefully long-legged hunters. How did these normally slow moving, unarmed browsers escape their enemies?"

An intriguing question. Obviously the various weapons of the other creatures were advantageous or they would not have evolved. Why then did the hadrosaurs not need them? Orthodoxy has it that they were caring parents and apparently moved about in herds, traits that could have given them sufficient advantage. Their strong social sense and protective instinct would have allowed them to proliferate into immense herds wandering the continents. There is safety in numbers as we see on what remains of the African veldt. Perhaps they just sacrificed the old, the infirm and the weak for the benefit of the rest.

Hadrosaurs showed explosive diversification shortly after descending from the iguanodonts towards the end of the Cretaceous. Extreme diversification depends on genetic variation. The greater the extremes, the more variation is implied and vice versa. Dinosaur extremes indicated great genetic variation which accounted for their ability to adapt and to radiate into vacated niches. The reason they could not cope with the events of 65 million years ago whereas they had successively coped splendidly with previous mass extinctions, the so-called Kimmeridgian turnover of 145 million years ago, the Aptian turnover of 117 million years ago and the Cenomanian turnover of 95 million years ago, was that in the few million years before the final act they had lost variation and had become inflexibly standardized. The last few million years of the Cretaceous showed a marked reduction in diversity of dinosaur species: the earlier vigorous adaptive radiation of the hadrosaurs and the ceratopsians similarly gave way to a yielding of variety. For the last two million years of the Period, a single genus of each – saurolophus and triceratops respectively – dominated the landscape, although they did so in vast numbers.

No gradual environmental change is going to eliminate genetic variation in genus after genus of dinosaurs. That very variation will guarantee adaptation to the changes by natural selection before genetic variation has been significantly pruned. The motive power of evolution is expansion of diversity with environmental change. The dinosaurs' loss of variety is much more characteristic of the loss of variety in species we are seeing today – by unnatural selection – at the hand of man.

Caches of bones of a single species are regarded by paleoanthropologists as suggesting husbandry. In the development of man, various cultures seemed to concentrate on ibex, horses, reindeer and so on. Could it be that ceratopsians and hadrosaurs were actually domestic animals like cows and sheep kept for food? Is it possible that hadrosaurs were the cattle of the Cretaceous period, herded on the great plains before being shipped to a Cretaceous Chicago for making into meat pies and hamburgers? Is it impossible?

CHAPTER TEN

ODDITIES IN THE ROCKS

"Look on my works, ye mighty, and despair!"

P.B.Shelley

Can a major civilization vanish with hardly a trace? What could one expect to find remaining of the world of Anthroposaurus sapiens? Dinosaurs are not just one species like man but a vast group of creatures which lived for millions of years – the modern equivalent is the whole of the mammals. Like the mammals only one dinosaur was likely to achieve intelligence. Just as remains of the intelligent mammal are scarce, one can expect the remains of the intelligent dinosaur to be scarce. Gribbon and Cherfas assure us: "The chances of finding fossils of an evolutionary variation that lasts only a few tens of thousands of years are slim."

Writer, Brad Steiger, in his book, "Worlds Before Our Own", develops the theme of the cataclysmic "seven worlds" legends of the Seneca indians. Much of his research supports the thesis of intelligent dinosaurs. The anthroposaurs might have *been* one of the "seven worlds"! Discussing the question of what would remain after an advanced civilization had been destroyed, he compares our own culture and technology with that of an ancient civilization. If a catastrophe were to happen to us now, he asks, what would remain for archaeologists to unearth 15,000 years from now?

He answers, "we are builders in wood and metal. Our most majestic stone buildings are little more than facades supported by thin tendons of steel. In a thousand years, even without flood, fire or nuclear warfare, our major cities would be little more than rubble... But if we were to enter another ice age and enormous glaciers should creep down from the north, as they have several times in the past million years, everything in their inexorable path would be pulverized."

And those scenarios take us forward only a fraction of the time that has elapsed since the demise of the dinosaurs 65 million years ago. In that time more than 60,000 feet of deposits would have been laid over our fallen cities. Without the continual folding of the earth the remnants of our civilization would be ten miles under the surface of the earth. But folding and erosion can expose these ancient rocks. They are then weathered and eroded anew. Even the most substantial of our engineering efforts like the Panama Canal might well have been worn away and redeposited as sediments several times in that timescale. Much of our works would have disappeared entirely, subducted under the fringes of continents by movement of crustal plates to be recrystallized millennia hence as new igneous rocks. It is not surprising therefore that only the most vestigial traces of the anthroposaurs remain today – and they may be deep in undisturbed strata. They might also be severely distorted, oxidized or mineralized, and might not be recognizable for what they originally were. Perhaps Velikovsky is correct when he writes, "prior civilizations are buried so deeply within the lower strata of the earth that we simply do not have any archaeological evidence of their existence."

Yet traces of the very substance of dinosaurs' bodies have been found. Carbon dust is found with some fossil dinosaur finds – the remains of the soft tissues, the skin, flesh and blood vessels. One wonders whether among it are any undecomposed molecules of the original protein or even DNA. Will we soon isolate DNA from the remains of dinosaurs to enable us to decide how advanced they were and even regenerate the creatures by gene culture (the theme of "Jurassic Park")? We might, but, meanwhile, such evidence as there is must be gleaned by raking through ancient rubble.

Although no one has been particularly looking for traces of civilization in rocks predating modern man, and although few traces of such a civilization can be expected, rock rakers, amateur, professional or incidental have nevertheless reported some distinctly anachronistic findings. There are probably yet more in the archives of museums of the world, waiting for some scholar to study and classify them. When geologists, paleontologists or archaeologists find objects in the wrong place, boulders miles away from their parent rocks or fossils embedded in solid rock, or in apparently undisturbed strata, which, in obvious terms at least, should not be there, they call them "erratics". Erratics are found at sites all over the world. Of course, objects like bones and fossils can get into strata in which they do not belong. An obvious example for human remains is by burial. But this is usually self evident – the deposits are obviously disturbed.

In 1878 a veritable graveyard of fossil bones of the large herbivorous dinosaur, iguanodon, were found 1056 feet down a Belgian coal mine at Bernisart, near Mons. At first glance this is curious because the coal deposits were laid down in the Carboniferous period almost 200 million years before the iguanodon appeared on the scene. But there was no cause for wonder. During the Cretaceous period the earth had cracked open into a mighty crevasse, an abyss stretching from the surface down to the coal deposits hundreds of feet below. Over many years, probably centuries, rain had washed Cretaceous mud and gravel into the huge crack and it had carried with it iguanodon after iguanodon. Paleontologists excavating the site found the crevasse stretched for hundreds of feet, and they eventually recovered 31 iguanodon fossils.

Bob Brain excavating in South Africa at Swartkrans knows only too well how rocks of different ages can get mixed together. He had been excavating a limestone cave in which parts of the roof had fallen to the floor. He worked out that on two occasions holes had appeared in the roof allowing surface waters to wash in rocks and debris for long periods. After the first occasion the sediments had sealed the aperture and a rise in the water table had then led to the leaching out of some of the deposits already there causing a multiplicity of new holes and channels in the, already jumbled, deposits. Holes in the roof had then again allowed fresh sediments to wash in filling the spaces left in the deposits already there. Finally part of the whole structure had been eroded away leaving the complicated mixture of deposits exposed as if a vast pit had been filled with crude concrete, a rock called breccia, made up of the mixed deposits. Complicated as it was, Brain had unraveled the sequence of events.

Thus, though it might be difficult to account for in detail, it is often clear when an anachronistic find has an explanation within the bounds of the current paradigm. There might indeed be conventional explanations for many of the examples quoted further on in this chapter – but they are certainly unusual. Some appear to date from long before mankind appeared on earth!

The study of fossil footprints may not sound as exciting as finding fossil bones but as R.S.Lull, a dinosaur hunter at the turn of the century, pointed out, footprints are fossils of living beings while petrified bones are of the dead. A humanoid footprint appearing at a time when there were no humans is bound to make you think. Yet reports of fossil human footprints are far from uncommon.

According to the American Encyclopedia, some rocks in Tennessee bear impressions of tracks of various animals and tracks of human beings "as visible and perfect as if they were made in snow or sand". The American Journal of Science of 1833 noted that a Mr Schoolcraft and a Mr Benton had observed prints of "human" feet in Mississippi limestone. An eminent geologist of the time stated they were "certain evidence that man existed at the epoch of the deposition of that limestone". Man? Whatever the views of some fundamentalist bible thumpers, man has unquestionably evolved from a common ancestor with the apes over about the last five million years. Human tracks could not appear in limestone – it is much older. But what if some species of dinosaur had evolved by convergent evolution into a man-like form? Isn't it possible that the footprints of such a creature, fossilized in the limestone but eroded over the intervening tens of millions of years could be mistaken for the prints of a human being? The eminent geologist goes on to say that the discoverer of the megatherium, Sir Woodbine Parish, had seen similar footprints in the rocks of South America. A man of his reputation is unlikely to get the age of his rock strata wrong. The impressions seen, although unquestionably human-like, must have been actually of some anthropic reptilian type.

The American Anthropologist reported in 1896 that the Ohio State Academy of Science had exhibited a large stone containing the print of a human foot 14 inches long. In 1975 Dr Stanley Rhine of the University of New Mexico announced the discovery of footprints human in appearance in strata estimated to be 40 million years old. Similar discoveries were made in Kenton, Oklahoma and in Wisconsin. Steiger relates yet another instance, an engineer called Johnson found footprints in an ancient sandstone near Tulsa. Johnson had had to remove earth and roots to uncover the fossils which evidently were human-like, and which were impressed in a block of sandstone weighing about 15 tons.

In the 1930s, Mr Roland T.Bird, who collected dinosaurs for the American Museum, introduced the world to a Lower Cretaceous site at Glen Rose, 80 miles from Fort Worth in Texas. The locals had discovered fossil footprints long before and Bird was startled to see the 20 inch tracks of a carnivorous dinosaur in the foundation stone of the county court house. Subsequently Bird uncovered a remarkable and now famous Cretaceous drama – the tracks of a brontosaurus being harassed by a large flesh eater. More interestingly still, a 16 inch footprint, described as man-like, and dinosaur tracks were found in strata of the same period.

In 1938 a Mr Berry and his companions found tracks of what appeared to be sabre tooth tigers, dinosaurs and three tracks of humans in the limestone bed of the Palaxy River. Since then many others have been found and an unknown number manufactured as the enterprising locals realized that fortune had provided them with the basis for a cottage industry supplying tourists with mementos. Fortunately the experts reassure us that they can comfortably distinguish the forgeries from the real thing. The "human" tracks seemed to show all the distinguishing features one would expect of a human foot bearing in mind that, coming from Lower Cretaceous deposits, they presumably were a hundred million years old, but they were 16 inches long. Humans could not have made prints of that antiquity, but we must respect the possibility of them being evidence of a human-like dinosaur.

Dr C.Burdick has publicized similar "human" tracks. Dr Burdick, it must be admitted, has his own axe to grind, being a creationist. He believes in the strict truth of the Biblical description of the creation and rejects the Darwinian hypothesis of evolution, modified or otherwise. Naturally, creationists like Dr Burdick would be delighted if the discovery proved to be of human tracks because the conventional evolutionary scheme does not allow for advanced mammals let alone human beings to be alive at the same time as the dinosaurs. Having said that, I presume that Dr Burdick would not deliberately be dishonest and fabricate relics to make his point. He describes "15 to 20 giant barefoot human tracks, each about 16 inches in length and eight inches in width". Sceptics maintain that the prints were those of giant sloths. But the spacing of the prints, initially six feet, widened to nine feet as the being apparently broke into a run, only the toes and the ball of the foot then being evident as would be expected of a running biped. Sloths were not noted for bursts of speed.

The largest and clearest tracks yet discovered were found in 1973. The footprints were described as 21 inches long, eight inches wide and five inches across the instep. The creature's stride was seven feet. The impressions are in the same layer of rock as tracks of the anatosaur, a duck-billed dinosaur.

Steiger comments that "if the tracks are accepted as human, then scientists will be forced either to place man back in time to the Cretaceous period or to bring the dinosaurs forward to the Pleistocene period". But this worst of all worlds stems only from the "acceptance" of the tracks as human. A more credible assumption altogether is that the prints are not human but are the fossils of tracks made by dinosaurs that had evolved by convergent evolution into a human-like form – an intelligent being, or its precursor, that evolved from the bipedal dinosaurs!

In October 1983 Steven Schafersman of the Texas Council for Science Education in a letter to "Geotimes" questioned the identification of the "man tracks" found alongside dinosaur tracks in places like Glen Rose. The genuinely fossil footprints he considered to be poor quality dinosaur prints in which mud had flowed back into the depressions altering their shapes or where the dinosaur had slipped making a track of odd shape. Others were not prints at all but random indentations containing several fossil worm casts wrongly interpreted as the ridges between toe prints. Finally there were fakes, footprint impressions deliberately carved in the soft limestone.

It is a pity that creationism is still an issue. Some creationists or their less scrupulous supporters are indeed willing to resort to fakery to disprove evolution by proving that men and dinosaurs lived on the earth together. What sort of a God do they have that requires his mortal devotees to fake fossils to defend him? Does he really advocate dishonesty? To the being that created the world in seven days surely a plethora of genuine fossil man-tracks should be no trouble if he felt they were necessary!

Schafersman, as a science teacher facing up to the creationists' fakery, is perhaps justified in attempting to write off the curious "man-like" prints. What of the contention, though, that the prints are indeed dinosaur prints but ones which have become "man-like" through structural convergence? Is this not a reasonable possibility – at any rate just as reasonable as the mixed bag of "explanations" thought up by Schafersman? Perhaps he is substituting bogusly creative answers for bogus creationist answers.

There are odder oddities. Inexplicable even by the super dinosaur theory are man-like tracks allegedly found in Carboniferous sandstone by Dr Burroughs of the Geology department at Berea College in the 1930s. He found ten man-like tracks and parts of others in strata of the Paleozoic era of 250 million years ago, millions of years before the dinosaurs and, in fact, when the highest species then evolved were the amphibians. Both left and right feet were seen with a step length of 18 inches. The prints found in Mississippi limestone mentioned at the outset seem to be from the same period.

Amphibians emerged near the start of the Carboniferous, about 400 million years ago, and radiated into many ecological niches over the roughly 200 million years of their dominance. They eventually died out at the end of the Permian period, about 225 million years ago when the reptiles began to assume their ascendancy. 200 million years may seems long enough for intelligence to evolve in a vertebrate lifeform but, if it did, one would expect to see it arise towards the end of the period, whereas these tracks (if the rock matrix has been correctly dated) are at least 50 million years too soon. More importantly, since the amphibians were cold-blooded, all the arguments formerly used against intelligent cold-blooded dinosaurs genuinely applies to them. Perhaps barefooted "gods" visited us in carboniferous times after all. Or have the creative Creationists been at work?

On 25 January 1927 in Pershing county, Nevada, a Mr Knapp found a fossilized shoe print impressed in rocks laid down at the time of the great reptiles. The double stitches in the seams were distinct, microphotographs showing them very clearly. "At one place it was double stitched and the twist of the thread could be clearly seen." The authenticity of the find was suggested by minute crystals of mercuric sulfide long ago deposited by leaching action in the impression. Such crystalline deposits can not realistically be imitated. A geologist of the Rockefeller Foundation confirmed that the substratum of the fossil was Triassic limestone.

In 1897, the Los Angeles Herald revealed that laborers had discovered a fossil shoe print in solid rock. The imprint was that of a shoe with a high narrow heel and a broad flat sole. It was so clear, in the fine grained shale in which it was found, that it looked as though "the owner had unwittingly put his right foot into soft mud but a day or two ago".

Sandal or moccasin prints have also been seen in the gypsum of the White Sands in New Mexico. Ellis Wright in 1932 found tracks of human form but

22 inches long. Some later tracks were accompanied by marks suggestive of the use of some sort of support like a walking stick by one of the antediluvian beings. The White Sands were laid down as an ancient inland sea gradually dried up around the time of the demise of the dinosaurs.

Oil workers have recovered carved bones and decorated "coins" from deep rocks brought up during well drilling. A gold necklace was found in a piece of coal. What appeared to be an iron tool was found in a Scottish coal seam. Two workmen signed affidavits to their amazing discovery in 1912 of an iron pot inside a large piece of coal that they were breaking up to be used in the furnace of a power plant. The pot left a clear fossil impression in the remaining pieces of coal.

Coalminers noticed a curious slab in an Iowa coal mine in 1897. Found 130 feet below ground just below the sandstone which capped the seam, it was approximately two feet long by one foot wide and was four inches deep. Its surface was inscribed with diamond shapes having the face of what seemed to be an old man in the middle of each. Steiger implies that the stone slab must have been 300 million years old. This puts it into the "super-erratic" category in that it preceded the death of the dinosaurs by over 200 million years and can hardly fit our thesis. But could it have been deliberately buried by a later race just as we would bury some sort of time capsule? Perhaps it carries a message meant to be decipherable by future beings. The features of the faces were said to be all similar, inclined to the right except for two of them, and, interestingly, all had a strange dent in the middle of their forehead. Was this the third eye (our pineal gland) which is most pronounced in some types of modern lizard – and possibly some dinosaurs too?

Steiger relates the story of a man whose grandfather in 1928 came across a concrete wall buried in a coal mine two miles below ground. While shot blasting a seam, the miner found, among the dislodged coal, blocks of concrete about a foot across. Although the broken edges showed that they were made of what passed as an ordinary sand and cement mixture, the faces of the blocks were highly polished. The remainder of the wall disappeared into the coal seam. Another miner working a coal face about 100 yards away struck what seemed to be the same wall. Mysteriously the coal owners pulled the men out of the coal faces and ordered them to keep quiet about their discoveries. What is more, before he joined that gang, a few years earlier, they had found a similar wall in a nearby pit. They had also found a cylinder of silver with staves imprinted on it, and a large bone described as being "like an elephant's". Wouldn't a layman easily mistake a fossilized dinosaur bone for an elephant's?

Another coal miner in West Virginia claimed miners had found a well constructed concrete building, and, astonishingly, a "perfectly formed human leg that had been changed into coal". Though the leg presumably was not human, it evidently was sufficiently human-like ("perfectly formed") to convince observers that it was human, with the implication that some human-like creature existed millions of years ago.

The June 1851 issue of the Scientific American described a metallic object blasted out of solid rock by workmen excavating in Dorchester, Massachusetts. The object consisted of "a bell-shaped vessel, 4.5 inches high,

6.5 inches at the base, 2.5 inches at the top, and an eighth of an inch in thickness". Although the article reported it to be made of a silver alloy which looked the color of zinc, a recent owner, in a letter to Steiger, says it is made of brass with iron and lead. It was inlaid in pure silver with six flowers and the base was also inlaid with what looks like a vine. The magazine described the chasing, carving and inlaying as "exquisitely done". Yet the vessel had been blown out of solid pudding stone, "fifteen feet below the surface... There is no doubt but that this curiosity was blown out of the rock" the article concludes. The origins of the vessel remain a mystery but man-made objects do not get embedded in rock so solid that dynamite is needed to shatter it.

Animal remains are rarely found in coal deposits because the conditions in the steamy jungles that gave rise to them promoted rapid decomposition. However Otto Stutzer describes in his "Geology of Coal" an apparently human skull in the coal collection of the Mining Academy in Freiberg. He does not mention the age of the coal deposits but says the skull is composed of brown coal and manganiferous and phosphatic limonite. Although there are deposits of brown coal in Russia that are from the Carboniferous period, brown coal is usually young coal from the Mesozoic era or the Tertiary period, the former of which covered the age of the reptiles!

The New York Times, in November 1926, reported that a Dr Siegfriedt who collected fossils for the University of Iowa, had found a "human" molar in coal deposits laid down in the Eocene epoch. Although the enamel had carbonized and the roots had mineralized into an iron compound, local dentists felt sure it was a human second lower molar. Dr Siegfriedt described the stratum as yielding many fossils for dinosaur research as well as sharks' teeth and fish scales.

In 1971 bulldozers moving earth for mine exploration revealed traces of human remains in soft sandstone said to be 100 million years old. The remains were underneath about 15 feet of material including "five or six feet of solid rock" and yet there appeared to be no caves or crevices in the overlying strata. Bits of bone and teeth were first found but then the excavators noted a more significant bone embedded in the rock. Local experts from the University of Utah were brought in and under their direction parts of two skeletons and a mixture of teeth and bone shards were uncovered. They described the skeletons as Homo sapiens. One of the bodies seemed to conform with the burial pattern of some Indian tribes. Oddly, the academic experts seemed to lose interest, moved on to other establishments and apparently never wrote up the find formally. But the bones were, on the face of it, the same age as the rock matrix. If the remains really had fossilized and were of an age comparable with the surrounding rocks, as some reports claimed, then this find would have been highly valuable in placing man-like beings in distant geological times. One wonders whether a close examination was made of the remains to determine whether the description of them as Homo sapiens would have held up. Or were the fossils assumed to be Homo sapiens because they looked human. Had the local experts only made a cursory examination, lost interest and moved on before rigorous anatomical studies had been carried out?

Let us step back a few years to a particularly interesting case. In 1898 two brothers said to be versed in "desert antiquities" found the fossilized remains of a "female", who was seven and a half feet tall, in the same stratum as fossils of "prehistoric camels and an elephant-like creature with four tusks". Fossils of palm trees, ferns and fish were also found. The curious thing about these "human" remains was that the "female" had a tail, having several extra vertebrae at the end of her spine. Our turn-of-the-century archaeologists surmised that Death Valley, where the fossils had been found, had once been on the continental shelf of the Pacific Ocean, and the fossilized lady's bones had been laid down at that time. Death Valley, like White Sands, lies in the Rocky mountains which were thrust up in a series of gigantic pulses through the Mesozoic and early Cenozoic eras, the very time when the earth was roamed by dinosaurs – until their extinction marked the boundary between the two geological ages. Could the large "female" with the tail be the best described specimen yet found of the man-like super-dinosaurs?

What though of the "camels" and four tusked "elephant" found with her? Isn't it quite likely that bones of small dinosaurs could be mistaken for those of camels and that bones of larger dinosaurs that had horns or tusks could be mistaken for the more familiar elephants? Even Mantell, when he reconstructed iguanodon from its remains, thought the thumb spike was a horn like a rhinoceros's. It is unlikely that any single specimen was complete, the remains were 65 million years old and, although, students of "desert antiquities", the finders were not professional paleontologists. The evidence may be better explained by our thesis of the intelligent dinosaur.

A letter to Nature in 1873 reported the discovery in Miocene strata of a fragment of bone probably belonging to a dinotherium and engraved with a picture of a horned quadruped and traces of several other figures. This discovery implies the existence of an intelligent creature capable of art work some 25 million years ago. Clearly, there must have been some misdating here. Though a dinotherium bone it could have been, an artist in the Miocene, long before men were around, it could not. The most likely explanation, that the artwork was of a rhinoceros and was by early man, would require the find to have been in recent strata. The alternative would be that the artwork was of a horned dinosaur and the relic was from the late Cretaceous rather than the Miocene. The bone cannot then have been that of a dinotherium. If the latter explanation prevailed, who could have been the artist in the age of dinosaurs other than our anthroposaur?

A Peruvian doctor, Steiger writes, has the unusual hobby of collecting stones – not fossils, but rocks bearing engraved pictures. The rocks, which were apparently discovered after a cave in, are claimed by the doctor to be around 60 million years old. But, since he would not reveal their source, it is a moot point whether the engraved markings are the same age. If they are then they are remarkable – they offer a detailed record of a strange race of beings of an alien culture doing things which, in some cases, we have only recently undertaken in our supposedly advanced technological society.

The engravings depict man-like beings along with creatures looking like dinosaurs including pterodactyls. The latter are apparently being ridden through the air by the man-like beings! The humanoid creatures seemed to have pointed tongues and noses beginning in their foreheads. They also seem not to have an opposed thumb but it is not clear whether this is a stylistic convention. The interpretation of one scientist is that some of the pictures show, in step by step illustrations, ancient operations including transplants of the heart and other organs, a Caesarean section and brain surgery. There were "operating tables... surgical knives, local and general anaesthetics, sutures and more... The figures were crudely drawn but the organs were masterpieces".

Unfortunately some investigators claim the engravings are forgeries. But examination of the stones did not show any evidence of power drilling even under 60 times magnification. Alternatively the scenes depicted may have been carved by native peoples in more recent times and show forms of human sacrifice including disemboweling rather than sophisticated operations. If they do prove to be genuine, or even if there is a core of genuine specimens which the poverty stricken local natives have found profitable to imitate, then they might offer evidence of an advancing, man-like but reptilian civilization at the same time as the last of the dinosaurs.

CHAPTER ELEVEN

HOW ARE THE MIGHTY FALLEN?

"Learn to see in another's calamity the ills
which you should avoid."

Publilius Syrus

The extinction of the dinosaurs is the "greatest of all titillating puzzles" according to writer, John Noble Wilford. Something unusual certainly happened at the end of the Cretaceous Period. Many genera of all kinds died off. Any terrestrial creature weighing more than 50 pounds as an adult became extinct; sea organisms of all sizes were devastated, including many minute sea creatures like the foraminifera; many of the sea bottom filter feeders such as bivalves disappeared; only about 30 per cent of sponges remained. But not all living things were equally affected:

- marine genera were badly affected but not freshwater ones;
- tropical plants suffered more than those in more northerly climes;
- pterosaurs died but not birds;
- most mammals survived but few marsupials;
- squid survived but their relatives the ammonites died;
- dinosaurs died but not crocodiles ;
- mammals, which were all small, and small lizards mostly survived but even the smallest dinosaurs died out.

Though the Cretaceous mass extinction was bad, the earlier Permo-Triassic mass extinction, when 70 per cent of all known types of animal became extinct, was worse. The Permian extinction is explained by the theory of plate tectonics. Several continents that had been slowly drifting separately around the globe crunched together creating the supercontinent of Pangaea. Most marine organisms live on the continental shelves but, where the continent buckled together, these were thrust up into mountain ranges leaving their inhabitants stranded. The mass of the new supercontinent also suppressed the welling up of magma at the mid-oceanic plate boundaries. Lacking the buoyancy of the underlying magma, the mid-ocean ridges then settled down under their own weight, increasing the depth of the oceans. Sea level fell as much as 200 feet, draining much of the remaining continental shelf and disposing of many more marine species. On land, species diversity was reduced because previously isolated species now met and only the fittest creatures were to survive the furious competition between them.

There is no such explanation for the extinctions at the end of the Cretaceous. By then the supercontinent of Pangaea had began to break up again and the continents were drifting apart slowly moving to their present positions. Alternative theories put forward to explain the Cretaceous extinctions often ignore the variety of species extinguished and cannot be credible. In our search for the truth behind the tragedy we shall examine some of these hypotheses, credible or not.

Exhibit 7. Genera surviving the Late Cretaceous extinctions.

	Before	After	Per cent
Freshwater vertebrates	36	35	97
Land organisms	226	183	81
Higher plants	100	90	90
Snails	16	18	112
Bivalves	10	7	70
Reptiles/Dinosaurs	42	8	19
Mammals	22	25	114
Sea surface micro-organisms	298	173	58
Sea bottom organisms	1976	1012	51
Swimming marine organisms	332	99	30
Ammonites/Belemnites	38	0	0
Nautiloids	10	7	70
Cartilaginous fish	70	50	71
Bony fish	185	39	21
Reptiles/Dinosaurs	29	3	10
All organisms	2868	1502	52

Richard Owen was the first to attempt a convincing explanation of the extinctions. He reasoned that dinosaurs (then considered to be cold-blooded) had thrived at a time when the earth's atmosphere was less rich in oxygen than it is now. The lack of oxygen disadvantaged reptiles less than it did mammals, therefore the reptiles dominated. When the air became richer in oxygen, mammals took advantage of their warm-bloodedness and higher mobility and saw off the dinosaurs. The theory could be persuasive but for the evidence. The oxygen content of the atmosphere was not lower in Cretaceous times than today.

Indeed analysis of air bubbles trapped in amber, the resin exuded by coniferous trees, indicates rather a higher oxygen level. These tiny air bubbles, which can give amber a cloudy appearance, are trapped when the resin hardens effectively becoming fossilized atmosphere. Air bubbles in Cretaceous amber apparently contain 30 per cent oxygen, nine per cent more than today, an incredibly high figure – the biosphere would have been unstable in respect of atmospheric oxidation. In our lower levels of atmospheric oxygen the lodgepole pine uses the instability of organic matter in the air as a weapon against competing species. The wood of this pine is so dense that it does not burn easily. The tree also has seeds which are able to survive fierce conflagrations. Yet the seasonal litter it produces, its pine needles and broken branches, are readily inflammable. Once enough litter has accumulated, it is liable to ignite and start a forest fire which wipes out competitors, leaving more space for the lodgepole pines and their seeds which survive the blaze.

Our atmosphere is rather delicately balanced. An increase in atmospheric oxygen of only four per cent, let alone nine, could be disastrous for us. At 21 per cent of oxygen a moisture content of only one sixth in organic waste prevents it from burning. But the probability of a spontaneous bush fire doubles for each 1.3 per cent rise in oxygen level above 21 per cent. Four per cent more oxygen increases the chance of a bush fire eight times: nine per cent more increases the chance of a bush fire 128 times. At 25 per cent of oxygen, plant tissue containing as much as a third water would burn easily. Even damp forests like the rain forests could ignite. Methane from bacteria prevents such a horror by removing each year 2000 million tons of oxygen from the air. Without this reaction the oxygen level in the air would rise by one per cent every 12,000 years and the earth would be incinerated after only about 50,000 years. It is unlikely that creatures in the Cretaceous could have coped with such conditions. The oxygen level in the amber must have been enhanced by some chemical or diffusion process not yet known.

Some theories are comical. Did you hear the one about the clever little mammals which surreptitiously robbed the nests of the dinosaurs who were too stupid to notice their disappearing eggs? Eventually no dinosaur reached maturity and they died out. This "theory" has several problems. First, we cannot be sure all dinosaurs laid eggs. We know that icthyosaurs did not. Nor can we believe the idea that the dinosaurs were stupid. Nor does it make ecological sense for a species to cause the extinction of another which is its source of food: if the hunted decline then so do the hunters – a balance is maintained. Finally and conclusively, this idea takes no account of the simultaneous deaths of other quite distinct genera including all those marine species.

Another joke is that flowering plants, the angiosperms, murdered the dinosaurs. The newly evolved flowering plants devised chemical weapons – like the alkaloids – that the stupid dinosaurs could not cope with. The dinosaurs could not understand such clever plants and continued to eat them causing their own extinction. Evidently the poisons evolved by the plants were very slow acting – dinosaurs proliferated for fifty million years after the emergence of the flowering plants, actually benefiting from them as a nutritious new source of food. Only then did they quickly decline. Nor does this idea explain the simultaneous extinctions in many unrelated species.

R.B.Cowles and others believe that the dinosaurs became sterile because a rise in temperature affected their testes. Sperm is sensitive to temperature, this being the reason why a mammal's scrotum sac hangs outside his body. Foklore has it that a man who wears underpants is less virile than one who does not. Possibly sterility rather than virility is meant, and so it might have been for the dinosaurs. A marked increase in temperature could have caused their extinction through infertility. Alternatively a higher temperature could have altered the sex ratios of their offspring. Incubation temperature affects the sex of present day reptiles and conceivably the dinosaurs' hatchlings could have emerged all the same sex. Similarly a loss of fertility caused by the rise in temperature at the end of the last ice age might have eclipsed the mammoths, mastodons and sabre toothed tigers. But is there any evidence for a sustained rise in temperature at the end of the Cretaceous?

Scientists on the oceanographic exploration vessel, The Glomar Challenger, examined rock cores taken from the ocean floor and indeed did discover a global warming 65 million years ago. They believed the reason for the warming was volcanoes spewing forth the "greenhouse gas", carbon dioxide. The greenhouse effect is the warming of the surface of the earth by gases trapping radiation from the sun. Carbon dioxide is transparent to the incident radiation from the sun but not to the longer wavelength heat radiation re-emitted by the earth. Carbon dioxide in the atmosphere traps the sun's energy and the earth's surface gets warmer. An increase of the gases in the atmosphere like carbon dioxide that are good trappers of heat radiation heats up the biosphere. D.McLean of the Virginia Polytechnic Institute has proposed that heating by the "greenhouse effect" is a likely cause of the extinction of the dinosaurs and would also have affected many other species. Measurements of the proportions of carbon-13 and oxygen-18 in rocks at the Cretaceous-Tertiary boundary indicate a brief sharp cooling followed by a longer warm period perhaps caused by a greenhouse effect.

Another group of theories blame the extinctions on an increase in radiation from space, whether from a weakening of the earth's magnetic shielding, by depletion of ozone in the upper air, from a nearby supernova or from an anomalous flair up on the sun.

Robert Uffen, Chairman of the Defence Research Board of Canada, reasoned that a weakening of the earth's magnetism would lead to extinctions. The earth's magnetic field deflects charged cosmic particles that otherwise would penetrate to the surface with seriously harmful effects. Periodically the earth's magnetic field undergoes a reversal which is quite sudden in geological terms but might actually take many, probably thousands, of years. The old field falls to zero then grows from zero in the reversed direction. On completion what was the magnetic north has become the magnetic south and vice versa. Note that only the magnetic field, not the earth itself, has reversed direction. A compass would point south if the present field direction reversed. The danger is not in the reversal itself, the direction of the field is unimportant, it is in the changeover period when the field strength is too low to prevent cosmic particles from hitting earth's lifeforms. The weakness in the theory is that the intensity of the cosmic bombardment can only double and though that might affect life on land it is unlikely to affect many of the species protected by water.

M.L.Keith, a professor at Pennsylvania State University, believes a depletion of the ozone layer in the upper atmosphere caused the K-T extinctions. His mechanism was the emission of excessive amounts of hydrogen chloride by volcanoes. The importance of the ozone layer is that it absorbs much of the incoming ultraviolet light. This high frequency light is healthy in small doses (being responsible for your holiday tan) but when more intense is very harmful, killing cells and causing skin cancers. Bare-skinned dinosaurs, like pigs and humans today, would have been vulnerable but furry and feathered creatures would have had protection, as would animals and plants dwelling in water below the surface layer. But we have seen that some dinosaurs had feathers and pterosaurs had fur. Other dinosaurs had scales. Feathers and scales would shield the soft skin beneath from the harmful rays.

A nearby exploding star, a supernova, would bathe the solar system in huge levels of radiation that would quickly put paid to many of the earth's inhabitants. Jacques Bergier, who with Louis Pauwels had most of Von Daniken's ideas about visiting gods a decade earlier, has even gone so far as to suggest that superbeings in space deliberately exploded a star to kill off the mammals' competitors, the dinosaurs. They thus broke an evolutionary bottleneck clearing the way for a surge in evolution leading to intelligent beings like themselves.

Unfortunately the pattern of extinctions does not match this idea. Photosynthetic algae like the coccoliths are very resistant to direct radiation, largely because they are unsophisticated organisms more difficult to damage than the higher organisms. Yet they were more severely affected than land based reptiles and dinosaurs. Then again marine animals would have been expected to survive the influx of cosmic rays better than land animals because water is an effective shield against radiation. Yet the extinction of marine organisms was more severe than that of land organisms.

Although cosmic radiation theories cannot match the pattern of extinctions, some authorities argue that the exclusion of visible radiation (ordinary light upon which all life depends through the action of photosynthesis by plants) for a year or more could match it. Absence of light would cool the earth and interrupt photosynthesis for long enough to destroy the larger animals at the top of the food chain. The most serious effects would occur in the oceans where the whole ecosystem depends upon photosynthetic plankton. Stopping photosynthesis in plankton for a year would undoubtedly have dire consequences with a clear likelihood of extinctions. Terrestrial animals that depend upon foraging for fruit or nuts or decaying matter could survive the darkness. Similarly plants which leave seeds around that are viable for long periods would be able to re-establish themselves when conditions improved again. The same is true of some of the plankton which can enter a dormant phase to wait for better times.

Whatever caused the global darkening would have to have been severe enough to cut down the light considerably because plankton can function efficiently, indeed more efficiently, at light levels of only a few per cent of normal daylight. Even if an ice age were triggered the plankton would be quite happy – maybe more so!

S.Gartner and co-workers in 1978 and 1979 sought the explanation of the extinctions in a sudden cooling. Their mechanism was that continental movements cut off the Arctic Ocean which effectively became a big inland sea or estuary with brackish or even fresh waters. Eventually the land barrier broke and the cold trapped water flowed into the more southerly oceans. The merely brackish water, though cold, would float on the warmer but saltier denser water of the oceans killing off lots of surface dwellers. Regrettably there is no sign that the Arctic Ocean was ever a freshwater lake. A sudden cooling could be the answer but a more convincing mechanism is needed.

Could volcanoes have triggered the cooling? Could they even have triggered an ice age? Louis Agassiz, the Swiss-American naturalist who studied under Cuvier, first discovered evidence of ice ages, or more explicitly "The Ice Age" (the most recent was originally thought to have been the only one) from his studies of the Jura mountains. Needless to say, orthodox geologists rejected Agassiz's idea for 25 years, preferring the Biblical flood as the explanation of the scratched rocks, erratics, and glacial tills he noted in the mountains. "The earth covered in ice... Absurd!" Now we know it was not absurd – volcanic eruptions can indeed cool the earth.

The year 1826 was long remembered as "the year without a summer." In the previous year an enormous volcanic eruption had occurred in Java. The volcano, Tambora, blew up in a cataclysm bigger even than the more often quoted case of Krakatoa in 1883. According to H. and E. Strommel writing in the Scientific American, the eruption reduced the height of the volcano by 4200 feet, and blew out 25 cubic miles of matter, much of it into the atmosphere. In the vicinity of the eruption, the miasma blocked out the sun so thoroughly that the blackness was "palpable". The explosion of Mount St. Helens in the North West USA bears witness to such a palpable blackness.

An extended period of continuous vulcanism on this scale could severely change the climate, triggering global cooling. But could it have destroyed the viability of the most successful animals the world had ever known? It is unlikely to have caused an ice age at the end of the Cretaceous. The earth's climate was not unstable then as it is now – it was not teetering on the edge of an ice age as it has been for the last few million years.

Plate tectonics cause ice ages. Through plate tectonics lighter rocks forming the continents drift on the heavier basaltic rocks below. From time to time a piece of a continent drifts over one of the poles and snow falls on its cool highlands. As time passes ice builds up until a vast ice sheet has been created. At the continental margins the glaciers calf into the sea as icebergs which drift into warmer waters, warming and melting as they progress. Melting abstracts heat from the surface water which is therefore cooled ultimately to 0 degrees Celsius. Salt water at 0 degrees Celsius is heavier than slightly warmer water, unlike pure water which has its maximum density at 4 degrees Celsius. The icy salt water therefore sinks to the depths, warmer water rises and the temperature of the whole ocean falls. On the shores of the polar continent the ocean freezes. When salt solutions freeze the ice which appears, apart from occluded salt (that trapped in tiny bubbles in the ice crystals), is pure, leaving a solution which is even saltier than before. The water gets denser, is obviously at 0 degrees Celsius and again sinks to the ocean's depths.

Once the icy water is at the bottom of the ocean the sun cannot heat it – it only heats the surface. Thus the oceans continue to fall in temperature as long as a continental mass remains near one of the poles. Emiliani has shown by isotopic methods that the temperature of the deep oceans has fallen monotonically from about 12 degrees Celsius to its present value of 2 degrees Celsius over the last 40 million years. The reason? – Antarctica is passing over the South Pole. At the end of the Cretaceous period 65 million years ago, the surface temperature of the oceans was 25 degrees Celsius almost as far as the British Isles. By ten million years ago surface water at this temperature did not get beyond the tropics.

At the time of the dinosaur extinctions no continent was at a pole, though Antarctica and Australia were near the South Pole. There were no vast ice sheets locking up water and calving off bergs. The earth was warmer and climatically more stable than it is now.

64 per cent of the sun's incident radiation at present gets through to the earth's surface. An increase in the reflectivity of the earth's atmosphere would cut the proportion below 64 per cent and the whole earth would become colder. Minute ice crystals in the upper atmosphere – the ones that cause halos round the sun and moon, mock suns and moons and so on – are highly reflective. By returning incident radiation to space, only a small increase in them could seriously reduce the sun's radiation getting to the surface.

Fred Hoyle shows that ice crystals of this sort form at temperatures below -40 degrees Celsius. But heat from the lower atmosphere normally prevents water vapor high in the air from reaching such low temperatures. The water vapor releases the heat as latent heat of condensation when it forms rain droplets. Rainfall of 25 inches (63 cm) supplies enough latent heat to prevent ice crystals from forming in the upper atmosphere but less rain would not provide enough heat to suppress crystal formation. Today the only extended regions where there is less than 25 inches of rain and this condition is met are the polar regions – exactly where the earth is cold enough for glaciation to occur. The average rainfall on the earth is about 30 inches (75cm), only 5 inches (12 cm) above the critical level. If it were to fall below 25 inches then ice crystals would form almost everywhere and a worldwide ice age would have arrived.

The cooling of the oceans as Antarctica passes over the South Pole has brought the risk of a freeze up within the bounds of possibility. Before about seven million years ago it was impossible. The earth's heat store is the ocean and the heat stored in the warm surface waters until then easily caused sufficient evaporation to put plenty of latent heat into the upper atmosphere. With warm oceans there is no chance that ice crystal formation could occur in the skies and therefore heat from the sun gets to the surface of the oceans, keeping it warm. It is a positive feedback system.

But once ocean temperatures drop so much that the threshold of ice formation is crossed a new feedback system starts to operate. Ice crystals in the upper atmosphere spread to lower latitudes cutting down the sunlight and cooling the oceans even more. Evaporation reduces further still and the ice crystals become more permanent. The land cools quickly and snow gradually builds up to form an icecap. When it is sufficiently large, glaciers start to calf into the sea, again cooling it and reducing the earth's store of heat. There is less evaporation, less latent heat transfer, more ice crystals form, less sunlight penetrates – a new feedback system locked into ice age has arrived.

Today the oceans of the world have a heat store of about ten years of sunlight. If the light of the sun were cut down for ten years it could switch on an ice age. Fine dust in the upper atmosphere could do it. It would mimic the action of the ice crystals, reflecting solar heat away from the surface of the earth. Fine dust of diameter less than a thousandth of a millimeter will stay in the stratosphere for long periods, certainly for a year but possibly for a decade or more depending upon the amount, its height and its size, and may be carried for hundreds or thousands of miles. The explosion of Thera in the Aegean Sea in 1500 BC carried dust to Egypt causing some of the plagues of Pharaoh at the time of Joseph. Very fine particles could stay aloft for a very long time indeed and, though they are not in themselves as effective as reflectors of heat as coarser ash or ice crystals, they can act as nuclei for ice crystals to condense upon.

The greatest volcanic explosion in the last two million years was the eruption of Toba in Sumatra 73,000 years ago. It was a hundred times bigger than the eruption of Krakatoa, throwing 500 cubic miles (2000 km^3) of dust into the air and creating a crater 25 miles (40 km) in diameter. Changes in the pollen in European sediments from this time show a marked cooling followed by a period of erratic weather and, after a delay of a thousand years, an ice age. This enormous eruption eventually triggered an ice age – but it failed to cause a mass extinction!

What then of Late Cretaceous times? Although a world wide drop in temperature did occur, there is no evidence of even a short ice age when the dinosaurs became extinct. As far as we know there were no icecaps, no calving glaciers and the oceans were warm. A Cretaceous freeze up did not occur because no highlands or landlocked seas were sufficiently near to the poles. Furthermore the heat capacity of the oceans was greater than it is now because little water was locked up as ice and sea levels were higher. The higher temperature and greater heat store in the oceans provided a greater safety margin over the possibility of an ice age starting. Instead of only ten years, 50 years or more of darkness would have been needed to trigger an ice age. Only in the last seven million years has the threshold of climatic instability been crossed which permitted the recent ice ages.

One explanation, it is claimed, can take in all the feasible theories so far reviewed – an asteroid of exceptional size hit the earth. Edmund Halley, of Halley's comet fame, suggested two and a half centuries ago that a comet had collided with the Earth gouging out the Caspian Sea and causing the Biblical flood. Billy P. Glass and Bruce C. Heezen revived the possibility of the earth having catastrophic collisions with cosmic bodies in 1967. They linked the fall of large meteorites with geomagnetic reversals, the extinction of species and the distribution of tektites (curious glassy droplets varying in size from several inches to microscopic, formed from molten rock projected through the air, and widely distributed over the earth). Lately the idea of a collision with an interplanetary body has been strengthened.

The Cretaceous-Tertiary boundary is marked by the virtual disappearance of the foraminifera, tiny creatures which live in the sea and whose shells of calcium carbonate, sinking to the bottom of the sea over millennia, form limestone. In the Gubbio district in Italy only a single species survived. Vast beds of Cretaceous limestone composed of foraminifera gave way to half an inch of reddish-grey clay which contained no fossils. Then another layer of limestone began. There was no sign of a reversal of the earth's magnetic field. This anomaly in the limestone rocks was found by Walter Alverez. His father, the late Luis Alvarez, a Nobel Prize winner, determined to estimate the age of the boundary layer. Micrometeorites shower the earth daily at a constant rate. Knowing that rate and analyzing the sediments for extraterrestrial material would show how quickly the sediments had deposited. Slowly deposited sediments should contain more interplanetary matter because it had been falling on them longer. He chose to look at iridium, a dense metal similar to platinum, rare on the surface of the earth (being dense, it had settled into the earth's interior when the planet was still molten, as did most other heavy elements) but more common in meteors.

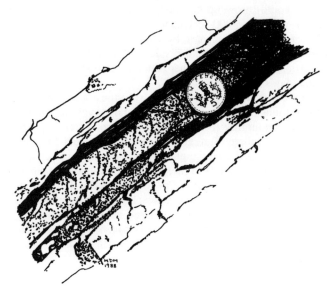

Exhibit 8. The Cretaceous/Tertiary boundary – only the thickness of a small coin.

Luis Alvarez was a specialist in nuclear activation analysis. A sample is bombarded with neutrons in a nuclear reactor until some of the elements present become radioactive. They can then be identified by their differing modes of radioactive decay. Alvarez's analysis of the clay gave odd results. The amount of iridium was 30 times higher than in the deposits above and below. The quantities were only a few parts per million but that is unusually large for rare elements like iridium, osmium and platinum. Tests on sites in different parts of the world gave similarly high concentrations. Other elements found in meteorites were also detected in comparatively high concentrations and tektites were present. The Alvarezes' believed tektites and meteoric materials confirmed that a massive meteorite, the size of an asteroid, had shaken the earth.

Scars on the surfaces of the Moon, Mercury, Mars, Venus and the moons of Saturn and Jupiter show they have been bombarded by meteorites throughout time. The earth also has traces of large meteor impacts in the form of craters, crater lakes or, in older weathered rocks, crater impressions. Only in 1908 some object from space (probably a fragment of the comet Encke) hit Tungusku in Siberia devastating a large area of forest. R.Grieve of the Canadian Department of Energy, Mines and Resources says that 5000 asteroids with diameters of more than 3000 feet (1 km) have struck the earth in the past 600 million years. Meteors 1000 feet in diameter have hit the earth every 10,000 years on average (corresponding roughly with the cycle of ice ages). G.W.Weatherill writing in Icarus in 1979 and E.W.Shomaker at the Snowbird Conference on large body impacts in 1981 have given the frequency of cometary impacts as – one km wide every 250,000 years, five km wide every 20 million years and 15 km wide every 100 million years. A 1000 feet wide asteroid would throw up one or two cubic miles of debris depending upon its entry speed. A 3000 feet wide meteorite would crash with a force equal to that of 10,000 ten megaton hydrogen bombs. It might be expected to leave a crater 12 miles across and displace 25 to 50 cubic miles of debris, more than sufficient to disrupt weather patterns and possibly enough to trigger an ice age in today's conditions.

The Alvarezes postulated an asteroid six miles across hurtling into the earth at 45,000 miles per hour, gouging out a crater over 100 miles across and shooting debris amounting to 60 times the asteroid's volume (8000 cubic miles) into the atmosphere. Sunlight would be blotted out for a long period, there would be prolonged cooling, photosynthesis would stop, the base of the food chain would die, animals higher up the food chain would starve. The asteroid must have approached more or less vertically. If it had approached obliquely spending more time in the atmosphere prior to impact, Allaby and Lovelock maintain it would have destroyed all life. Friction would have heated the air to such a temperature that nitrogen and oxygen would have reacted forming nitric acid, sterilizing the earth with its corrosive and oxidizing action.

Exhibit 9. Lake Manicougan, Quebec drawn from a Landsat photograph

Astronomers have observed suitable objects. The Apollo class of asteroids are prime candidates. They include planetoids of the right size and they cross the earth's orbit making it likely that they would collide with the earth from time to time. But where is the crater? Only one large impact crater has an age of 65 million years, Manson Crater, recently found underneath sediments in Idaho, but it is too small to have caused destruction on the scale envisaged. It is only 20 miles across not the 100 miles that would be needed. Conceivably the asteroid broke into fragments on entering the atmosphere and the Manson Crater is the scar of just one of the fragments. Some scientists argued that the asteroid was most likely to have fallen into the sea, vaporizing huge quantities of water, causing torrential rain for months on end, and a temporary greenhouse effect. No crater would then be obvious. If the asteroid disintegrated before impact some fragments might have landed in the sea and some on land, adding to the complexity of the climatic effects. Others said that the meteor would have made a crater even though it fell into the ocean, but this has now been subducted under continents by the action of plate tectonics. About half of the ocean floors have disappeared under the edges of continents and reformed at the mid-ocean ridges since the end of the Cretaceous period.

"But there is a crater," said others "or a scar of one at any rate." Fred Whipple, the originator of the dirty snowball theory of comets, largely confirmed by Giotto, claimed that the impact was so energetic that the earth's crust shattered allowing vast amounts of magma to well up filling and destroying the crater but leaving a massive scar still volcanically active – it is Iceland! Iceland has no rocks more than 65 million years old. The volcanic "hot-spot" under the Hawaiian chain of islands in the Pacific was suggested as an alternative point of impact but that is unlikely. It seems to have been active for too long, at least 80 million years. Recently a crater has been found in the Yucatan peninsula and is considered a prime candidate but, like the Manson crater, it seems too small.

The Alverez team used the idea of a cosmic collision to encompass four previous explanations: (1) suppression of photosynthesis – the global darkness of three to six months curtailed photosynthesis and led particularly to extinctions in the oceans; (2) the greenhouse effect, especially of an impact into the ocean – the temperature rise caused by a blanket of water vapor would have killed many land animals; (3) an ice age – exclusion of the sun's radiation for many months would lead to a global cooling which would kill off many species; (4) pollution and poisoning – the impact heated the air to such high temperatures that large amounts of nitrogen oxides were created by chemical reaction between the normally inert nitrogen and the oxygen in the air, and the acid rain, which subsequently fell, devastated life for a long period afterwards.

Some scientists were not convinced that the meteorite impact could trigger mass extinctions any more than a large volcanic eruption could. Would the debris thrown up stay aloft long enough to cause any lasting damage? After all many genera and individual species did survive showing that, despite darkness, dust and poison gases, conditions could not have been bad for too long. A fairly short period of darkness could explain the excessive extinction of water dwelling species relative to land types because the food reserves of the plankton in the sea is only sufficient to last for between ten and a hundred days, but land plants can suffer the absence of light for longer. A period of darkness of three years, as the Alverezes supposed, would have destroyed most genera, perhaps all higher ones.

Many species were not seriously affected – and many others, we know, had been suffering decline before the hypothetical collision. According to E.G.Kauffman of Colorado University, 75 per cent of marine organisms were in decline at the end of the Cretaceous period. They had been on the wane for two to five million years and few species seem to have died off at exactly the same time. Ammonites had fluctuated in population previously. Some ammonite genera declined and expanded periodically while others seemed relatively steady. When extinctions had occurred before, the steady species had tended to survive while the fluctuating species had died off. In the upturn the steady species had radiated into available niches including those suiting the fluctuating species and the cycle continued. At the end of the Cretaceous the ammonites were in such decline that there were no reliable steady species to bring them through. What was different? What had killed off the steady species of ammonites?

Dinosaurs were similarly on the wane and by the end of the Cretaceous survived in numbers only in the West of North America, having died out in South America and possibly Europe. Even in North America the decline was severe. Half of the 36 genera of dinosaurs alive about ten million years before the end of the Cretaceous had died out by the time the final million years was entered. Robert Bakker is among those who do not support the catastrophe theories: he claims there is no doubt that dinosaurs did not die out in a geological instant but petered out over thousands if not millions of years. Plainly life was under stress. What was its cause?

Leigh Van Valen and Robert Sloane attributed the extinctions to climatic changes over the last five to ten million years of the Cretaceous. At the beginning of the period vegetation was prolific and typically tropical or sub-tropical: towards the end of the period the climate had become typically temperate with cool woodlands. Dinosaurs thrived in the warmer climate but in the cooler one mammals had the advantage. The proposed reason for the change in climate was that the ocean floor had lifted with renewed mid-ocean spreading and sea levels had risen. Shallow seas divided North America and also divided Europe from Asia. Ocean currents and wind patterns may therefore have altered.

On the other hand, Bakker argues a fall in sea level draining the shallow continental seas could have triggered the mass extinctions. This accounts for the loss of a lot of marine species, those preferring the continental margins and intra-continental seas obviously, but the loss of light warm water draining from them on to the ocean surfaces would also lead to the demise of many open sea species that could not adapt to the colder surface conditions. What though of the land vertebrates? Surely they would have had more lebensraum and should have multiplied. No. The linking of previously isolated continents by land bridges created conditions similar to those in the great Permian extinction – hypercompetition between species and the unchecked spread of disease and parasites in populations not adapted to be immune from them. Large active animals like the dinosaurs could migrate faster, therefore they experienced more competition and disease, and suffered most. Smaller creatures like the mammals could migrate, but more slowly, having more time to adapt and freshwater species, which seemed least affected, could not migrate, though they were affected to a lesser extent by pests or diseases carried in by the migrants. Late in the Cretaceous some Asian genera of dinosaurs appeared in North America having crossed the Bering Straits (or whatever the dinosaurs might have called them) showing the two continents had linked. A more recent example was the land bridge which formed between North and South America, about 30 million years later than the dinosaurs, when many South American species failed to survive competition from invaders from the North.

Bakker puts particular emphasis on the spread of diseases unrestricted by hereditary immunity. Warm-blood is at the ideal temperature for bacteria and viruses to multiply. The warm-blooded dinosaurs would therefore be susceptible to the new pathogens being introduced to all the continents. He quotes examples like the spread of the Black Death and the carrying of rinderpest from India to Africa with devastating effects on the antelope herds. V.D. and smallpox devastated the Amerindians. Virulent strains of myxomitosis were deliberately developed by CSIRO in Australia and introduced into the wild to control rabbits. All have depended upon the intelligent mammal with its capacity for travel and his insensitivity towards other species. Bakker contradicts his advocacy of the evolutionary resilience of the dinosaurs. The dinosaurs, he persuades us, are great competitors and the forming of land bridges, while leading to mass extinctions, also provides lots of empty niches for enterprising species to adapt to. If the theory is true at all, and it might be partly true, we need to know why the genetic variability of the dinosaurs had been reduced to such an extent that they could not cope with the new challenge as they had always done before.

Those doubtful of the Alverez's theory thought the iridium anomaly could be explained by differential sedimentation rates or volcanic activity. Further careful testing of the iridium layer showed that the iridium concentration seemed to build up slowly during the last few thousand years prior to the supposed cataclysm. Volcanic activity occurring over an extended period, they argue, would be more likely to match such a pattern. India had broken from Africa and raced (in geological terms) across the Indian Ocean to hit Asia. The collision pushed up the Himalayas and created such friction that lava spewed forth for centuries to form the Deccan Peninsula. This was the extended vulcanism they sought.

Calder noted that 65 million years ago in Western North America plants were "dusted with exotic elements". Besides iridium, volcanoes emit other metals present in the K-T sediments not commonly present in meteors, like arsenic and antimony. For Charles Officer and Charles Drake of Dartmouth College this proved the boundary layer and the extinctions were related to the break up of the old continents. The level of the seas fell to their lowest for 200 million years. The warmth which gave subtropical conditions to northerly climes subsided. Widespread volcanic activity over a long period (but short on a geological timescale) led to pollution, climatic changes and ecological damage which destroyed species.

You will, by now, have noticed that some experts have postulated high sea levels and others low sea levels as reasons for the Cretaceous extinctions. You may well ask: "Don't they know where the sea level was? Wasn't it where it usually is?" Sea level provides a riddle of its own. Geologists, notably those working for oil companies have built up a detailed knowledge of changes in sea level over the ages. In the last 200 million years it reached its highest consistent level from about 85 to 67 million years ago when about twice the area of continental shelf presently inundated was flooded. In the preceding 100 million years sea levels had steadily risen due to the activity of the mid-oceanic ridges and the sea floor spreading associated with continental drift. The welling up of magma under the mid-oceanic ridges displaces the water of the oceans causing higher sea levels.

Sudden unexplained falls in sea level occur periodically but are rarely linked with meteorite falls. The sudden onset of an ice age freezing large amounts of water in extensive ice sheets might explain some recent sea level changes but not those in the Cretaceous. They also do not normally coincide with mass exterminations, throwing doubt on an idea like Bakker's. The sea level did fall rapidly about 67 million years ago, the event identifiable with Bakker's theory, but there was a greater fall in sea level 95 million years ago which is associated with only a minor turnover of species compared with the extinctions terminating the Cretaceous. Why did this earlier event not have the impact of the later one if Bakker's idea is correct?

Any convincing explanation of the extinctions has to account for all the genera that became extinct not just those that are representative of the dinosaurs. It also has to be sudden, at least on a geological timescale. The dinosaurs had shown that they were well able to adapt over 140 million years and were still evolving in the Cretaceous. A gradual change of conditions was unlikely therefore to overwhelm them – they would have adapted into the new conditions. Though doubt is being cast on the asteroid impact, many of its anticipated effects like adverse climatic disturbance and pollution of the environment remain persuasive – but were these the shadow of an asteroid or did they come from closer to home? Today we see similar effects created by the intelligent mammal. Volcanoes and asteroid impacts do not have to be invoked to explain the environmental problems we are experiencing, or the mass extinction of species currently taking place. Similar things are happening today to events at the end of the Cretaceous.

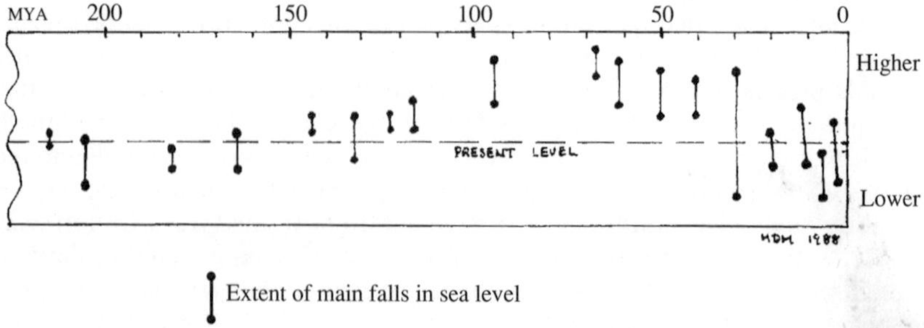

Exhibit 10. Changes in sea level over the last 200 million years (after Calder – see bibliography)

CHAPTER TWELVE

LESSONS IN EXTINCTION

"People could survive their natural trouble all right if it weren't for the trouble they make for themselves."

Ogden Nash

Charig, in his book, "A New Look at the Dinosaurs", listed 30 likely causes of dinosaur extinction. He then listed less likely causes – poison gases, volcanic dust, meteorites, comets, sunspots and wars. Yet today, one of these, the meteorite or comet theory, is accepted by many as the unequivocal cause of the Cretaceous terminal event. An unlikely solution has become a certain solution. Why shouldn't it change again and favor instead poison gases and wars?

Perhaps the seeds of change are already germinating. Robert Bakker, we saw, is one of the authorities who do not accept the asteroid idea. Beverley Halstead of Reading University, England, who died in a road accident, was another. Halstead had a brilliant but outrageous reputation. He once perched for a photograph naked in a tree, his genitals dangling below him. He also shocked and amused dinosaur enthusiasts at a conference by demonstrating with his girlfriend how dinosaurs could copulate despite their long tails. And Halstead believed that late Cretaceous dinosaurs *did* need help in reproducing – only twelve species remained when the end came. Dinosaurs were already virtually extinct and had been in decline for five million years before the supposed fall of the asteroid. Professor Anthony Hallam of Birmingham University, England, denies that an asteroid struck at all. Having closely examined the strata in the boundary layer, he believes that the iridium had been laid down over thousands of years, not a few months as a cosmic collision demanded. If the decline of the dinosaurs was associated with the iridium deposits, it was certainly not a sudden event.

What *does* seems indisputable is that many of the mechanisms of extinction reviewed in the last chapter and expected of a cosmic collision sound uncomfortably close to what we see about us today, the result of high technology and too many human beings demanding too much of the earth's resources with no thought of the consequences. I have argued that the dinosaurs had the wherewithal to become intelligent. Did one species of dinosaur gradually kill off the others and finally itself?

Wilford doesn't think so. "Wondrous as they were the dinosaurs were limited. They were incapable of causing their own extinction, or of foreseeing and preventing it." Yet today we are in the midst of a mass extinction before which that of the late Cretaceous seems to pale. "Basic processes of evolution are being altered more drastically than since the sudden disappearance of the dinosaurs, and possibly more than since the emergence of life's diversity," warns ecologist Norman Myers in his book, "The Sinking Ark". In the future, would our descendants or another intelligent species wonder about the mass extinctions at the end of the Tertiary? Would they notice our little conceit, the Quaternary – it would be only millimeters thick, like the K-T boundary layer? Would they realize that the extinctions had been caused by just one species, either deliberately or through carelessness? Our record proves that we are killers. Perhaps the anthroposaurs were also.

We began killing other species a long time ago – and not just for food. Although mammoths, mastodons and woolly rhinoceroses had survived several periods of intense cold in previous cold phases of the present ice age, only at the end of the last one did they go extinct. A variety of catastrophic explanations for this have been suggested but, more likely is the simple explanation that they were hunted down by man.

The Miocene period of about 20 million years ago was the age of the apes. Today only five species, including man, remain. Only man is populous. Don Johanson and Maitland Edey say "we are responsible for the disasters that have recently overtaken all modern apes". Carl Sagan is more explicit: "humans have systematically exterminated those other primates who have displayed signs of intelligence... We may have been the agents of natural selection in suppressing the intellectual competition". We have confined the gorilla, the chimpanzee, the orangutan and the gibbon to narrow areas and within our lifetime they could be extinct. We will have murdered our intellectual rivals.

More obvious intellectual rivals had already been disposed of by our ancestors. The dismembered remains of 50 adult giant baboons and several juveniles were unearthed at Olongesailie in South West Kenya. With them were hundreds of chipped stones from a site 20 miles away. Clues that tool-users brandishing weapons killed these animals comes from the presence of percussion flakes from toolmaking and cut marks on the bones. Baboons are powerful animals. With their strong jaws they do not need to make stone tools. They also live in bands. The hunter that had disposed of them must have been skillful and far from cowardly. He apparently had only primitive tools to face ferocious troops of giant baboons. The hunter was the first true man, Homo erectus – the giant baboon is long extinct.

Anthropologists have found stone tool fragments alongside Australopithecus remains suggesting that A.africanus was the tool maker. But the stone flakes are the same as those made by Homo erectus. The implements found with the australopithecine bones were discarded by Homo erectus after dinner. The australopithecines were extinct 1.4 million years ago, caught between the predatory attentions of Homo who found them easy game (just as slow as Homo was himself and too unsophisticated to defend themselves adequately) and the baboons who had no particular predatory intentions but competed more successfully for food.

About two million years ago mammalian evolution went into overdrive and the number of genera of mammals trebled in the next million years. The diversity of mammals peaked about one million years ago. Since then it has continuously declined as mankind became increasingly dominant. Most mammals other than domestic animals will be extinct within decades. Compare it with the Cretaceous. Bakker writes, "It took no more than two million years – maybe much less – to exterminate the dinosaurs."

The prehistory of mankind has many examples of apparently unnecessary killing. Were men even in those early days as insensitive to other species as they appear to be today? At the foot of a limestone cliff at Solutre, France, was a 50 feet deep mound of horse bones, killed by prehistoric man. Dr Sandra Olsen of the John Hopkins Medical Institute, Baltimore, examined the remains of animals killed by early man on sites like this, 35,000 years old, and showed that only seven of 3000 bones, mainly reindeer, had cut marks on them caused by butchery. So few signs of cutting could only signify that prehistoric men had not killed these animals primarily for meat. The experts decided they had killed for delicacies – liver and intestines. Maybe. Or maybe they just killed for fun! Maybe they got high on the smell of death. At any rate the slaughter continued for 25,000 years. Carl Sagan tells us, "shortly after man entered North America via the Bering Straits there were massive and spectacular kills of large game animals, often by driving them over cliffs". Like their contemporaries at Solutre, these emergent men used the same technique, but thousands of miles away. Mass carnage was widespread and effective.

Civilization does not seem to alter us. Quite the opposite! Humans have savagely hunted down the animals with which they share the globe since they discovered technical ways of compensating for their puny bodies. In historic times humans have exterminated many varieties of animals and birds, though some of them, like the bison, existed in vast numbers. Myers highlights the rapidly increasing rate of destruction as technology has improved: "as a primitive hunter, man proved himself capable of eliminating species. From the year AD 1600, however, he became able, through advancing technology, to over-hunt animals to extinction in just a few years." The rate of extinction of species of mammals and birds (not counting lesser creatures and plants) increased from one every four years from 1600 to 1900 AD to one every year in most of the present century. By 1974 writers in "Science" magazine considered that 1000 species of all kinds were becoming extinct every year. If the tropical forests are substantially cleared "by the end of the century we shall have lost one million species, possibly many more. Except for the barest handful, they will have been eliminated by the hand of man" (Myers).

This compares with estimates of one species every 1000 years during the mass extinction of the dinosaurs, though the latter must be a serious underestimation because very many species existed – and died – without leaving any remains. Millions of creepy crawlies must have died without trace – and plants. And, for those we do know about, there must also be some degree of averaging over a long time period of much more sudden extinction events because of the generally poor resolution of time in old rocks. When the time resolution is better because deposition was copious, we find that extinction in the Cretaceous could occur extraordinarily rapidly – for some species at least. J.Smit and J.Hertogen found that there were no significant changes in the deposits of foraminifera species for over 600 feet in the K-T boundary layer, representing millions of years in time, but they disappeared in a fraction of an inch representing "about 200 years". Mankind's ability to kill off marine and aquatic species in bulk has developed since the start of the industrial revolution about 200 years ago.

In addition to the wanton destruction of species, human proliferation has created a huge imbalance in faunal variety illustrated by the huge human biomass of 250 million tons – probably greater than that of any other animal species. And, besides the six billion human animals, there are their domesticated animals – three billion domestic herbivores. What we see is a reduction of species variety together with an increase in actual numbers of some animals. That is just what happened at the end of the Cretaceous.

A large predator will not hunt mice. The reward is not worth the effort. Nor would men be expected to bother with small prey. The pattern of extinctions of mammals in the last million years shows that so far 50 per cent of large mammals have gone but only two per cent of small mammals have. This too is similar to the extinctions at the time of the dinosaurs. But if mankind did not hunt them, why have some small mammals died out? Effects tend to knock on. Norman Owen Smith of Witwatersrand University in South Africa, has proposed that overhunting, which caused the extinction of the larger herbivores, led also to the loss of open ground. The lack of the herds allowed the bush to grow in to the grasslands again. Since the smaller herbivores, which lacked the size to keep the forests at bay, were also disadvantaged by the spreading bush, they also lost ground and became extinct. Thus although mankind did not hunt the smaller animals his overhunting of the larger ones indirectly caused the downfall of some of the others.

But some opportunistic small species like the sparrow and the rat make a virtue of the environment created by man. The same thing happened in the Cretaceous when birds and some inconspicuous rat-like creatures thrived in the disruption of the environment created by the anthroposaurs, and then survived their demise to colonize the world – the birds and our ancestors, the primitive mammals.

A future student of the rocks, looking back on the terminal extinction at the end of the Tertiary would see extinctions starting much sooner in Europe and Africa than in the Americas. Diversity would seem to continue for longer in South America where man did not arrive until much later. In the Triassic the dinosaurs of Asiamerica were diverse and abundant but elsewhere they seemed static and conservative. Could that suggest that the primitive but emerging anthroposaur did not get to Asiamerica until late but that his unwelcome attentions held back the evolution of species elsewhere from an earlier time?

Many of the main theories of the death of the dinosaurs boil down to the effect of pollution, the source of which was impacts with asteroids or erupting volcanoes. Maybe the truth was more mundane – the anthroposaurs drowned themselves and their planet in their own waste, just as we are doing!

Pollution is a symptom of increasing entropy, a scientific measure of disorder. By creating greater order in constructing themselves, lifeforms reduce entropy within their bodies and perhaps in their immediate surroundings but in so doing they vastly increase entropy in the world at large. The more such creatures there are, the more disorder, the more entropy, they create. When the entropy of their world gets too high they die. Entropy is waste. Organisms trapped in a sealed environment with plenty of food quite often poison themselves to death on their own waste. A ferment of home brew will stop working even though there is plenty of sugar and nutrient left. The yeast is poisoned by the alcohol that it makes as waste. The anthroposaurs poisoned themselves on their waste. We are doing the same. The earth is effectively a sealed environment and if we fill it with waste products we shall die.

Entropy is sewage. Sewage destroys life in surface water as bacteria decompose it into carbon dioxide thus removing dissolved oxygen. More oxygen can dissolve in the water from the air but, when sewage pollution is heavy, replacement can be a lot slower than consumption. The oxygen gets used up and life in the polluted water dies of suffocation. In inland and shallow continental seas, the leaching out of soluble inorganic fertilizers like nitrates and phosphates adds to this effect. They promote the growth of surface algae in unpleasant masses, blocking light from the water below and adding to the oxygen demand when they decay.

Entropy is acid rain. The final Cretaceous atmosphere was acidic. The source of the acidity, we are told, was either volcanic emissions or the formation of nitrogen oxides as the death star burned its way through the air prior to impact. Dramatic! Reality could have been as commonplace and stupid as it is today. Anthroposaurs pouring acid into their environment, as we are doing, would not have survived long. Greenland core analysis shows that the air today is four times more acid than it was in the 16th century. This modest ratio disguises the fact that local levels close to the source of the acidity were much higher. Moreover, the pH scale of acidity is logarithmic not linear. This means that a change in pH of one unit from say 6 to 5 represents an increase in acidity on a linear scale of ten times: every unit reduction in pH is another ten-fold increase in acidity. Rain which has fallen in the industrial parts of the world tested to be pH 4 is a thousand times more acidic than pure water which is pH 7.

But it is not only the acidity itself that causes damage. The geographical extent of the acid damaged forests in Germany increased from eight per cent to more than 50 per cent in only a few years. Though this loss of forest is distressing enough, the main danger to higher animals comes from the acid leaching out the salts of heavy metals, which then poison the ground water. Entropy is pollution by heavy metals. Each metal has a threshold level of acidity below which it remains bound in the soil but beyond which its salts dissolve into the water. According to Bernhard Ulrich, a West German chemist, toxic aluminium ions begin to be released from the soil into the water when the pH reaches 4.2. Aluminium is now being linked with senile dementia, Altzheimer's disease. Did the dinosaurs suffer from premature senile dementia caused by acid rain?

How are we creating this acidity? Mainly through industry: burning fossil fuels and sintering metalliferous ores to extract the metals. The by-product is sulphur dioxide, a noxious gas that eventually turns into sulfuric acid, one of the most corrosive mineral acids. The top ten sulphur dioxide polluting countries in the world in 1980 were emitting 100 million tons of sulphur dioxide a year.

If anthroposaurs reached an advanced society they must have added acids to the air and thence to the groundwater. It takes 5000 years for the world's groundwater to replenish. If it became a poisonous soup of acid and heavy metal ions, it would be 5000 years before it became usable again. Even in the Cretaceous, with its higher rainfall, it could have remained polluted for 1000 years. The poisoning of the earth's groundwater could be a very effective way of initiating a mass extinction.

Plenty of heavy metals are associated with the end of the Cretaceous and the death of the dinosaurs. The experts say they came from metal bearing meteorites or local volcanoes. But if human beings are anything to go by, an intelligent creature can easily produce enough heavy metals to pollute the environment without having to resort to natural causes. Nature causes 325,000 tons of copper to leach into the world's water supply every year, but humanity annually extracts 7.5 million tons of copper and most of that will finish up as waste. The figure is increasing.

Cores from the Arctic ice cap show that lead in the air is now 500 times its natural level, the increase having principally occurred since the industrial revolution. Lead is a cumulative poison – it is stored in the body until danger levels are exceeded. Our own bodies contain more than 1000 times more lead than our recent ancestors. Lead poisons the nervous system and the brain by interfering with enzymes. Young minds are particularly affected. The symptoms, at dosages that may well be far below the official toxicity level, are distractibility, impatience, frustration, restlessness, impulsiveness, destructiveness and violence – symptoms typical of the behavior of much of our urban youth!

The clay band of the Alverez's does not only contain iridium; it is full of heavy metals. Other metals in the boundary layer at abundances higher than normal are osmium, palladium, arsenic, chromium, cobalt, selenium, nickel and tin. These metals are not only found in extra-terrestrial sources. Terrestrial sources such as copper-nickel ores and molybdenum sulfide ores also contain many of these unusual metals, concentrated naturally by molecular filtration which traps the metal in the crystal lattice of the basic material of the ore. But such mechanisms occur in particular localities and cannot account for a worldwide distribution. If, though, these metal ores had been mined, smelted and processed to get at the copper, nickel or molybdenum, the flue gases would have carried off the remaining metals to pollute the environment widely.

The concentration of the metals in the boundary layer varies from place to place just as one would expect from sites that might have been close to, or distant from, an industrial area. Furthermore ores from different sources, processed in different places, would have had different compositions so the analysis of the boundary layer in different places would be expected to vary as researchers have found. A death star would have a fixed composition and would distribute its components fairly uniformly. Death stars may be more romantic but common industrial pollution fits the description better.

When heavy metals are around, the natural responses of the earth can make things worse. Professor Frederick Challenger of Leeds University, England, has shown that organisms rid themselves of unwanted or poisonous elements by converting them into their methyl derivatives which, being volatile, disperse into the atmosphere. Marine algae get rid of mercury, lead, antimony and arsenic in this way, not to mention sulphur and iodine in large quantities. Dispersion of the latter elements is beneficial to organisms on land since without it they would suffer from sulphur or iodine deficiency. But methylated heavy metals are very toxic. Methyl mercury was the agent of severe poisoning at Minimata in Japan where, for many years, a factory discharged mercury wastes into a bay which provided seafood for the local people. In the West farmers using organic fungicidal dressings on their seeds get better yields because the grain does not rot in the ground. They also poison thousands of birds. The fungicides contain mercury.

Historians suspect that Napoleon died of arsenic poisoning from the arsenic salts used as a pigment in his bedroom wallpaper on St Helena. Fungi growing on the damp walls disposed of the unwanted arsenic by converting it into volatile methyl derivatives which the would-be emperor inhaled, slowly poisoning himself. The authorities have banned a similar compound of tin used in an anti-fouling paint for boats because it causes genetic damage in shellfish.

Entropy is chemical pollution. Companies in the USA use over 60,000 chemicals and more than 13,000 of them are known to cause genetic damage. In the modern world dangerous poisons are bandied about like confetti, and supposedly all in a good cause. For every human being on earth, the world's farmers apply a pound of pesticides to their crops every year. H.K.Erben of Bonn University noticed that the eggshells of the species of dinosaur he was studying got thinner in more recent deposits. Pesticides like DDT and polychlorobiphenyls (PCBs) harm animals at the top of a food chain by absorbing into body fats and accumulating in the predator as it eats its prey. If sufficient accumulates at some point in the chain, the animal suffers physiological damage leading to death. Predatory birds, like eagles, have suffered notably. Their eggs become so thin and brittle they break in the nest. Bakker classifies birds as living dinosaurs!

Cancer-causing PCBs are never found in nature but are found in the bodies of 99 per cent of Americans. The sperm count of the American male is only half its value in 1940. The reason why is not known. What *is* known is that in the same period increasing amounts of organochlorine compounds have been found in sperm. Organochlorine chemicals kill pests so why shouldn't they kill sperm? An expert tells us that dinosaurs died out because mammals killed and ate their young: another tells us that their young were all born the same sex. What if their young were not born at all because pesticides had sterilized all the males? Do our manufacturers and governments care if pesticides sterilize the human race? Though PCBs are still widely used, advanced countries have banned DDT but still manufacture it for export to other, mainly Third World countries!

Every year industry dumps 250 million metric tons of dangerous waste that can "cause cancer, birth defects, miscarriages, nervous disorders, blood diseases and permanent, possibly fatal, damage to the liver, kidneys or genes," according to James Bellini. But dangerous quantities don't have to be large. Daily each of us takes in one millionth of an ounce of vinyl chloride mainly from PVC. But Italian researcher, Cesari Maltoni, has demonstrated that only one part in a million of vinyl chloride causes mammary tumors in rats, and only 25 parts in a million causes cancers of the liver. Those are single doses. Continuous exposure to doses of only one tenth of these levels have similar effects.

Farmers bathe the land with chemicals. Many have the simpleton's philosophy that, if a little fertilizer is good, a lot must be better. They pollute the water table, waste their money and destroy the quality of the soil. Loss of quality, through loss of fine particles, organic matter and water, reduces rooting depth which, paradoxically, results in less fertility. Poor quality soil coheres badly and therefore erodes more easily. David Pimentel, Professor of Entomology and Agricultural Science at Cornell University says that loss of soil depth is seriously reducing food production. The US is losing soil at seven tons an acre each year; a third of the topsoil has been lost in only two centuries of farming.

Because of overuse of fertilizers our lakes and rivers suffer from eutrophication. Prolific growths of algae and photosynthetic bacteria, thriving on the excess nutrients washed out of the soil, suffocate everything else by their excessive oxygen demand as they decompose. Organic deposits forms thick layers on the bottom, quite unable to be oxidized but eventually metamorphosed by anaerobic bacteria and then pressure to yield hydrocarbons. Our main oil deposits today were laid down in the Late Cretaceous. Oil was originally formed in shallow, stagnant lakes or seas on continental shelves. The conditions were those of eutrophication. Did the stagnant waters of the lakes and shallow seas polluted by the anthroposaurs provide the conditions for the formation of the Cretaceous oil deposits? Perhaps a close analysis of the original oil bearing rocks will give us some indication of how polluted the environment was and where the pollutants originated from, whether excessive amounts of silt were brought down, and whether it has any characteristics that show the soil had been cultivated. Our farmers and industrialists are setting up suitable conditions. Could we, in such places as the Great Lakes and the Baltic Sea be initiating the next phase of petroleum formation?

The "greenhouse effect" is another recurrent theme in the demise of the dinosaurs. The planet certainly got warmer. From the ratios of oxygen-16 to oxygen-18 in limestone laid down at the time of the K-T boundary layer, the ocean temporarily warmed by between one and five degrees Celsius then a long term cooling set in.

Most climatologists expect major changes in our climate during the next fifty to one hundred years. The concentrations of greenhouse gases in the air are increasing and the temperature of the earth is rising at a corresponding rate. In 1985 scientists released figures based on the analysis of air trapped in polar ice sheets. The concentration of atmospheric carbon dioxide was 270 parts per million (ppm) by volume from the 15th century till the beginning of the 20th century, enough to keep the temperature of the earth comfortable rather than the -25 degrees Celsius it would be without it. Since then it has risen to 350 ppm by volume in less than a century. Methane is a greenhouse gas twenty times more powerful than carbon dioxide. Over the last 300 years the amount in the air has doubled and it is now increasing at a steady rate of one per cent per annum. The UN Environmental Protection Agency in 1984 tentatively predicted a rise of five degrees Celsius by 2100 AD. Tom Widgley of the Climatic Research Unit of the University of East Anglia, England, calculates that the natural greenhouse effect will have doubled by 2027 at the latest. Temperatures would rise between two and four degrees as a consequence.

The direct effect of greenhouse heating is that water will evaporate faster: it will have less time to penetrate into the soil and more water will evaporate from rivers, streams and lakes. Consequently the water table will fall and the land will get much drier. Climate will be more continental with hotter, drier summers and colder, harsher winters. Extended land masses, including the wheat growing areas of the US and the former USSR, will become more arid – the bigger the land area, the more pronounced the effect. A rise of only four degrees Celsius could destroy the wheat producing areas. In contrast lands adjacent to ocean margins, especially where there are mountains, will be exposed to very heavy rainfall due to the high evaporation from the warm sea surface.

A warmer planet will mean that the permafrost of Siberia and Canada will melt releasing methane trapped there forming a positive feedback loop pushing temperature higher still. A rise of four degrees Celsius might be enough to start to melt the polar icecaps. The reflectivity of the earth near the poles will fall, more heat will be absorbed and another disastrous positive feedback loop will form accelerating the melting. The icecaps contain 98 per cent of the earth's fresh water and could lift sea levels by 160 feet. The rise could be even greater because the earth beneath the Antarctic would rise as the weight of ice was released from it displacing even more water.

Besides fossil fuels burnt for energy the main source of increasing atmospheric carbon dioxide is the destruction of forests for grazing. The tropical wet forests cover almost 10 million square miles and keep vast amounts of carbon bound up that would otherwise be atmospheric carbon dioxide. Yet satellite photographs show that farmers are clearing 0.5 per cent of these forests each year, an area the size of Wales. In August 1987, the US satellite NOAA detected 8000 separate fires at least a million square yards in size. The release of this bound carbon is building up carbon dioxide in the air at the same rate as the burning of fossil fuels. Clearing the forests also alters the reflectivity of the surface, changing convection currents and air circulation, decreasing rainfall in the tropics, increasing it in latitudes up to about 40 degrees, and decreasing it in the temperate latitudes beyond. The earth's climate will be more like it was in the Cretaceous period!

In Cretaceous times the anthroposaurs had plenty of fossil fuels because the great coal making era was the Carboniferous starting 300 million years earlier. Plenty of oil lay in the rocks from the Jurassic Period almost 100 million years before. And Cretaceous forests were also burnt. Thick deposits of carbon have been discovered in New Zealand and elsewhere associated with the Cretaceous terminal event. Was this carbon from forests being consciously burnt?

Carol Greitner and William Winner of Oregan State University have shown that, although plants normally take up more carbon-12 than carbon-13 during photosynthesis, in polluted air the carbon-13 take up is more closely in balance. The ratio of C-12 to C-13 remains as a permanent record in the tissues and can be used to test conditions at the time. Is the carbon dust found with some late Cretaceous dinosaur fossils richer in C-13 than would be expected? Is Cretaceous oil richer in C-13? Carbon released from burnt forest might give an apparently contradictory picture. Limestone laid down at the time has less C-13 than C-12 apparently signifying that the air was less polluted. But it could be that there was more C-12 in the air. If anthroposaurs burnt forests and fossil fuels then a large amount of old carbon of biological origin would enter the atmosphere. Because the carbon would have been fixed by photosynthesis at a previous period when the air was unpolluted, it would be relatively richer in carbon-12. The proportion of carbon-12 in carbon dioxide circulating in the air and the oceans would therefore increase. Naturally then the proportion of carbon-12 incorporated into limestone from the shells of the foraminifera would also increase.

A similar phenomenon is occurring today. Old carbon is entering the air and old carbon contains less carbon-14, the isotope of carbon used in carbon dating, because it decays radioactively. Very old carbon in fossil fuels contains none. Carbon-14 is produced continuously from the impact of cosmic rays with nitrogen in the air and therefore is always present at a steady concentration. But its concentration in the air is starting to drop. Old carbon from the burning of forests is beginning to dilute it.

Though the average Brazilian consumes less meat each year than a domestic cat in the United States, he has to slash and burn forests to satisfy our demand for steaks and hamburgers. A habitat which harbors perhaps 50 per cent of all species is destroyed to make pastures for one species, cattle, and food for one other, man. The fall in variation of the hadrosaurs at the end of the Cretaceous might indicate they were herded. Could the anthroposaurs have burnt their own forests to provide more nutritious browsing for their "cattle"?

If the atmosphere in the late Cretaceous were gradually polluted its effects should show up in the fossil record as an adaptation of species to the pollution. Poisonous fumes or particles of dust in the air would induce the development of unusual nasal arrangements to attempt to prevent the pollutants from penetrating to the lungs.

Ankylosaurs were armored dinosaurs living at the end of the Cretaceous. They were related to a similar group called the nodosaurs which lived principally in the middle of the Cretaceous period. The earlier group had nasal passages consisting of a simple paired tube leading from the nostrils to the back of the throat. The ankylosaurs however had nasal passages stretched out into the shape of a letter 'S' on either side of which there were additional passages forming almost a honeycomb. Teresa Maryanska has suggested that the purpose was to filter and moisten the air before it entered the lungs. Yet why should elaborate filtering systems have been necessary at the end of the Cretaceous but not apparently beforehand, even in closely related species, unless something was happening to the air? Other species from distant parts were equally affected. Iguanodon orientalis from Mongolia had a huge bulbous nose supported by a bony arch.

Crested and non-crested hadrosaurs were contemporaneous about 75 million years ago. By the end of the dinosaurs' reign 65 million years ago the crested hadrosaurs were particularly successful. The crests were either enormous plates or long projections having no ostensible use. The odd thing about the crests however was that they consisted of enormously extended nasal passages protected by the bone of the skull. There must have been evolutionary pressure to extend the nasal passages, and the skull had solved the problem of where to accommodate the resulting labyrinth by developing the crests. The evolutionary pressure was pollution.

Exhibit 11. Did the hadrosaurs evolve elaborate breathing apparatus to protect themselves from atmospheric pollution?

The external shape of the crest did not always match the internal convolutions of the nasal passages suggesting that the external appearance was as important as the elaborate nasal extensions. Were they also visual signalling devices for courtship and mating? Hadrosaurs had acute vision judging by their well developed eye sockets and the presence of a bony ring (the sclerotic ring) to support the large eye. Several species of hadrosaurs seemed to inhabit the same territory and the visual signals could have served to distinguish them. They could have served to signal their position in the social hierarchy and probably the sex of the animal. But why did the nasal passages extend to serve these purposes unless some other cause had stimulated their development? Having started to develop a feature for one reason it is characteristic of sexual selection to make a virtue of necessity and use it for another.

David Weishampel of Florida State University has shown that the cavities could have also acted as resonance chambers for audible displays or communication. Other hadrosaurs without crests probably had inflatable sacs over their nostrils which served the same purpose and could have also served as a visual display. And such sacs would have developed as a protection against pollution in the air. Thus two distinct groups of hadrosaurs had different solutions to the same problem but one solution left obvious fossil records whereas the other has to be inferred. The development of nasal flaps and convoluted nasal passages is best explained as an evolutionary response to increasing atmospheric pollution. Once the protective measures had began to evolve these dinosaurs found that they had other uses too. That is typical of the way evolution works.

Evidence from the elaborate display apparatus of the ceratopsians and the hadrosaurs, and the signs of ritual duelling in pachycephalosaurs (and possibly ceratopsians) indicates that the dinosaurs were by this stage if not before, territorial and "possessive". The pachycephalosaurs had high bony heads that they probably used in pushing contests or butting contests to assert dominance rather as sheep and goats do. The elaborate frills of the ceratopsians, besides serving a defensive purpose and as an anchor for the massive jaw muscles, were probably display devices to signal dominance and might have been brightly colored. These animals might also have engaged in ritual duelling by engaging their horns and grappling rather like rutting stags. Bakker's contention is that such active sexual behavior is a sign of warm-blood.

If the anthroposaurs were as territorial as mankind then we could expect them to engage in conflict and, if their society became technical then the conflicts could have been huge, just as mankind's World Wars were – about 20 million people died in the first World War and about 55 million people in the second. The severity of wars have grown exponentially like population and we can expect several hundred million deaths as a very minimum if another world war started. Many of the symptoms of our own time were displayed at the end of the Cretaceous. What of nuclear war?

Any advanced society worth its salt will have discovered the equivalence of matter and energy. Did the anthroposaurs? John Noble Wilford tells us that "uranium and dinosaurs are often found together. The bones soak up and concentrate the uranium in the mineralization process." Perhaps there are less prosaic reasons for this association.

Evidence of prehistoric nuclear combustion has been found by French scientists in Gabon, West Africa. Uranium consists of different isotopes, mainly Uranium-235 and Uranium-238, which are normally found in constant ratios in any uranium deposits. Only U-235 is suitable for atomic reactors, and it is just this isotope that the ore lacks. It is depleted in U-235 just as if the reactive isotope had been extracted leaving the "waste" Uranium 238 and some other rare elements. The scientists' explained that the isotope had leached out and spontaneously reacted in a natural atomic pile. But it could equally have been deliberately extracted. The deposits are far older than the Cretaceous but neither do we extract valuable minerals from deposits that are being laid down today. The anthroposaurs were tapping rocks laid down long before they appeared on the scene.

What would our waste ponds at atomic weapon factories and nuclear power stations look like in 65 million years? What would the remains of the Chernobyl atomic reactor look like when the passage of time has eroded away the concrete and the radioactive residue has permeated the surrounding clay? Perhaps in these instances too there might be some spontaneous reactions, chemical and physical which the geologists of 65 million AD will believe have occurred naturally.

The nuclear power industry depends upon nuclear fission which generates hundreds of types of highly radioactive elements as waste materials. Some are intensely radioactive but have short half lives and become depleted if stored for a few years. Many others are radioactive for anything from thousands to millions of years. The USA has millions of gallons of high level waste, that will be radioactive for millions of years. Some of it was stored at West Valley in storage tanks that were not expected to last for more than 35 years!

High level waste from the Manhattan Project, the development of the wartime atom bomb, was dumped on to land surrounding the town of Canonsburg, Pennsylvania, and apparently forgotten. Then local citizens became alarmed as many became afflicted with and died of a variety of cancers. Tests showed soil on the playing field of the local high school had radiation readings 700 times the background level.

Besides high level waste there are also large amounts of low level waste that is not so intensely radioactive though some of it may also be active for long periods. In fact there is evidence that nuclear plant operators have diluted high level waste until it could be falsely described as low level waste. Low level waste surprisingly often "accidentally" seeps into the ground or streams. Thus it is conveniently disposed of. If the secret got out, the experts will reassure us it is "only low level waste".

By the year 2000 AD there will be 2000 tons of plutonium stockpiled and 160 tons a year being produced, all in "civilian" reactor programs. Twenty pounds is enough to make an atomic bomb. Criminals or fanatics who got hold of this small amount of plutonium could make a bomb. It would not have to be well designed or efficient. Even a nuclear damp squib could cause horrific damage especially in a populated area. It would spread so much radioactive contamination that it could be worse than an atomic blast.

Only 45 years after the first nuclear reaction, mankind has some 600 nuclear power plants in operation. Rosalie Bertell, a cancer specialist, calculates that 13 million people in the world have died of fallout since the War. That does not include the effects of Chernobyl. If there were a nuclear war, a hit on a nuclear power station would produce a very dirty blast indeed. All the fission products of the nuclear reactors' cores would be vaporized and sent high into the atmosphere to cause fallout never before seen by mankind. Long-lived radioisotopes would pollute the earth for hundreds of thousands of years. Each power plant destroyed in this way would be equivalent to an extra 25 megatons of nuclear bombs in killing potential, though the damage would be spread in time.

Scientists have noticed at nuclear test sites in sandy areas that one effect of the atomic blast is to fuse the sand into a green glass. Yet glass of this type is found throughout the globe in certain geological strata. Steiger asks, "could it be possible that these sites provide evidence of a prehistoric nuclear war?" Droplets of molten glass are found in the K-T boundary layer. One might wonder whether any of the late Cretaceous sediments contain unusual amounts of long-lived nuclear isotopes or their decay products.

Advocates of the asteroid theory point to stress lines in pieces of quartz, stress lines that have only been noted in quartz in four different circumstances, one being in the residues at the Cretaceous-Tertiary boundary. The other three instances are in the laboratory produced by tests, in known meteorite craters, and on the Nevada nuclear test site. The expert's argument goes: "We have found stressed quartz; we know it occurs where meteorites have fallen; therefore a meteorite fell. (Oh, the same effects can be made artificially in the laboratory or by nuclear bomb blasts, but we all know those are irrelevant in this context.)"

Though pollution can damage forests much worse damage would occur from nuclear attack and fallout. Pine trees protect themselves against damage by exuding a resin which subsequently hardens and becomes amber. An explanation of the large amounts of amber found in some parts of the world could be that radiation or pollution severely damaged or stressed pine forests leaving the trees exuding their natural defensive substance in large quantities. After the disaster at Chernobyl, scientists studying the effects of fallout on coniferous forests found that the trees quickly absorbed dangerous radioactive cesium and incorporated it into their wood. But not by the root system – cesium sinks only slowly into the soil and it would take 25 years or more for it to begin to be taken up this way – pine needles directly absorbed the radioactive elements. Thus radioactive cesium is absorbed rapidly through pine needles and more slowly through roots subjecting the trees to severe stress for a long period but without necessarily killing them. When the trees eventually did die long lived isotopes would return to the soil to continue their damage in succeeding generations. Amber is variously dated. Baltic amber is usually dated in the Oligocene epoch of about 30 million years ago but the Eocene epoch of 55 million years ago is also given. Valchovite, the amber from Czechoslovakia, is dated to the late Cretaceous period, the time of the extinction of the dinosaurs.

Radioactive emissions preserve. A dinosaur "mummy" hadrosaur discovered by Charles Sternberg died 65 million years ago, lying on its back apparently unharmed and with no signs of predators or scavengers having touched it. It is odd that it did not decay or get eaten. Supposedly it dried out in the sun, got swiftly washed downstream and got covered with fine mud so quickly that its dried skin had no time to rehydrate and decay. Dinosaur mummies are rare, but when found they are usually late Cretaceous hadrosaurs. Why should they have died so perfectly and been preserved? Because they died of gamma radiation and neutrons which preserved them as surely as it would preserve strawberries in a plastic bag?

Failure of photosynthesis is another mechanism of dinosaur extinctions. Dust from the crashing asteroid or erupting volcanoes cut off the light and heat of the sun, preventing plants from making sugars and cellulose from carbon dioxide and water. Plants would die then animals would starve, and if the darkness continued for long enough whole species would become extinct. It could happen today. Some scientists wrote in 1984:

"...clouds of fine particles would soon spread throughout the Northern Hemisphere, absorbing and scattering sunlight and thus darkening and cooling the earth's surface. Continental temperatures could fall rapidly – well below freezing for months, even in summertime... We have only recently become aware of how severe the cold and the dark might be... agriculture, at least in the Northern Hemisphere, could be severely damaged for a year or more, causing widespread famine... humans would die from freezing, starvation, disease, and the effects of radiation... the extinction of many plant and animal species can be expected, and in extreme cases, the extinction of most non-oceanic species might occur..."

They were warning the Pope of the dangers, not of volcanic eruptions or asteroid impacts, but of a nuclear winter following a nuclear war. They concluded: "Nuclear war could thus carry in its wake a destruction of life unparalleled at any time during the tenure of humans on earth, and might therefore imperil the future of humanity."

Quite. And did the anthroposaurs actually do this 65 million years ago to cause the Cretaceous mass extinction of species? If a nuclear war could cause extinctions now, why shouldn't a nuclear war among anthroposaurs have done the same then? Luis Alverez himself in 1982 drew the parallels between the asteroid collision and a nuclear war. A major exchange of bombs on the scale we have them at present could release the same energy as the fall of a 1000 yard wide asteroid. The asteroid would concentrate all the impact in one spot and be capable of blowing chunks of terrestrial matter high into the atmosphere, even out into space. A nuclear exchange would not put as much matter into the high stratosphere, but what did go up would be more evenly distributed geographically, and might also be spread out over a period of time. Chicago University scientists found deposits of carbon distributed world wide in the iridium layers. Apparently there had been extensive and intense fires. The fires would have darkened the skies with dense smoke and poisoned the air with incompletely burnt carbon forming the deadly poisonous gas carbon monoxide. Couldn't atomic warfare have ignited these fires? Was there a nuclear winter?

A sudden cooling certainly did occur. The coal layer at the end of the Cretaceous Period marks a distinct change in climate. In the more recent rocks above it are cool climate plants like the giant sequioa; in the older rocks below it are subtropical plants like ferns and cycads. Is this layer of coal a fossil of the nuclear winter?

In 1962-63 southern England experienced its coldest winter since 1740. The cause was a peculiar meandering of the stratospheric jetstream, a fierce continuous blast of wind which influences weather patterns even though it is itself above the weather zone. Over Britain the jetstream pushed arctic air further south. 1962 marked the culmination, prior to the implementation of the nuclear atmospheric test ban treaty, of an enormous escalation of atmospheric testing. About 20 megatons were tested in 1958, but in both 1961 and 1962 the tonnage tested was about 200 megatons. K.Y.Kondratyev, the former USSR's leading atmospheric scientist says that the tests severely disturbed thermal radiation in the upper atmosphere leading to four per cent less sunlight reaching the surface. The Russians were particularly concerned because one result was that their grain harvest in 1963 was disastrous. The attenuation of the sunlight was the result of the production of brown nitrogen oxides in the nuclear fireballs. And that was only with 200 megatons exploded over deserts or oceans such that dust and smoke were not created.

A nuclear winter is not in the realms of fantasy. Smoke and dust do not have to be sent into the stratosphere to prevent the sun's rays from reaching the surface – nitrogen oxides do the job quite well, though any serious nuclear conflagration will provide smoke and dust aplenty as well as brown fumes.

Another reason offered for the downfall of our dinosaurian predecessors is radiation from space. We do not need supernovas or any such explanations for the danger that we face today from radiation from space. Few people will be unaware of the hole in the ozone layer observed over the Antarctic. More recently one has been noted in the Arctic and it is getting bigger. The March 1985 edition of the "UN Environment Program News" stated that "ozone depletion could seriously affect many life forms". Ozone blocks the entry of high energy UV radiation to the earth's surface. UV causes blindness and skin cancer in humans.

The agents destroying the ozone layer are CFCs, chlorofluorocarbons. We release CFCs into the air faster than nature degrades them. They react with UV radiation in the stratosphere to give free radicals which then trigger a chain reaction breaking ozone into ordinary oxygen which has no protective value against UV. Each 2.5 per cent rise in CFC concentration causes an extra million skin cancers. The World Wide Fund for nature claims that the extra UV reaching the earth's surface is killing phytoplankton, the primary food source of the oceans. The CFCs are also particularly powerful greenhouse gases, 1000 times more effective than carbon dioxide. Dr Robert Watson maintains that the ozone layer will continue to reduce for the next fifty years whatever we do because of the chlorine already released. International Conferences calling for cuts in production of CFCs can apparently achieve nothing in our lifetime. We can only take measures that might benefit our children!

Burning tropical forests contributes also. The amount of smoke produced from the fires in the Amazon region, according to Dr Alberto Setzer of Brazil's space research institute, is equivalent to a hundred volcanoes erupting. Professor Paul Crutzens, Head of the Max Planck Institute at Mainz and one of the world's leading experts on the ozone layer, says these fires are among the main causes of ozone destruction. The peak of Amazon burning is in August. It takes about ten days for the smoke to penetrate the stratosphere and travel south. The peak of Antarctic ozone erosion occurs from September to November.

Maybe the soot layer in the K-T boundary zone reported from New Zealand and elsewhere indicates that the anthroposaurs destroyed their ozone layer and left themselves exposed to deadly UV radiation. Again one feels justified in asking whether today's events have been experienced before by the earth.

I have tried to convince you that an intelligent dinosaur could have destroyed much of the life on earth at the end of the Cretaceous. Many facts support the hypothesis. Moreover we can see the intelligent species with which we are familiar – ourselves – creating conditions that seem to mirror those that were so destructive then. Needless to say, experts often find it hard to see.

James Lovelock and Michael Allaby, experts on the biosphere of the earth, sound like public relations executives for the polluters. They insist they do not wish to ridicule "legitimate concern" about the state of the terrestrial environment, but simply to "place in perspective the puny attempts of industrialists and farmers" in polluting the environment. They compare them with what nature has done in the past through glaciations, volcanic eruptions and meteoric collisions. Despite all of these natural disasters, whose scale dwarfs the attempts of man, life continues. There is no need to worry about human pollution – the earth has been able to cope with far worse. All species modify their environment just by being alive. Mankind is no different and cannot degrade his surroundings to the point of extinction. They conclude, "Our power to destroy the world, or even ourselves, is quite imaginary, a product of our hubris."

Yet elsewhere Lovelock argues that the control systems of the earth would break down if the human population were to reach ten billion. Mankind would then desperately have to artificially maintain what formerly were self regulatory feedback systems. We would no longer have a natural environment that sustained life but a "spaceship earth" with life support systems provided by the occupants. Unless, that is, we succumb to "gigadeath", in which case mankind will have done – simply through procreating – what these same experts claimed was "quite imaginary, a product of our hubris." And why chose ten billion as the danger level? What if he has overlooked some factor and the figure is five billion? Then the threshold has already been crossed and we are passengers of spaceship earth without realizing it. Experts have unquestioning faith in their own pronouncements no matter how arbitrary they may be. Yet we accept them.

Lovelock seems genuinely full of concern when he writes: "Each time we significantly alter part of some natural process of regulation or introduce some new source of energy or information, we are increasing the probability that one of these changes will weaken the stability of the entire system, by cutting down the variety of response". Bravo! Surely urgent action is merited to make sure we do not increase the probability that some danger point is exceeded. What does he recommend? No need to panic – there is "ample time and every inclination on the part of scientists to investigate and prove or disprove allegations, and then leave it to the law-makers to decide rationally what should be done". Aaaargh! He wants to involve a cabal of experts. Not only are the scientific experts to mull and ponder over the diagnosis but the political experts are then to debate it in the legislature and legal experts are to test it in courtrooms. Too bad if the patient is in terminal decline.

Others are less sanguine. Dr Hans Martin says we do not have time "to develop our skills. We are presented with a curriculum which includes primary and secondary school, university courses and graduate studies simultaneously". In the imagery of Dr Stephen Schneider of the US National Center for Atmospheric Research: we are staring into a murky crystal ball and cannot clearly foresee the future; if we waited five years hoping the ball would clear, the vision awaiting us would be all the more horrific. Their message is evident. We have no time to study, no time to understand the cybernetics of our environment. There is no time to decide what we can safely do. Deterioration continues daily. We must call a halt to the damage now. But we may already be too late!

None of this hubris worries Allaby and Lovelock but something else does: "The credible threats must come from outside the earth and the impact of a large planetismal is the most immediate of them... We have a moral obligation to take such modest, inexpensive steps as we can to avert them..." An asteroid impact that occurs perhaps once every 26 million years, if their interpretation of the fossil record is correct (and the next is not due for some 13 million years), is far more worrying than the destruction being wreaked every second by mankind!

Can't you picture the Professors Expertosaur, 65 million years ago saying exactly the same thing? And worse, convincing their compatriots that they should examine the skies and muse on the best ways of saving life on earth by deflecting planetismals while everything died about them. The meteor never came but the anthroposaurs fooled observers 65 million years later into believing it had, by simulating all its symptoms.

We are all, let alone the experts, indifferent to the fate of the earth – evidently the anthroposaurs were too. Like the anthroposaurs, we do not seem to have grasped that we are also on the list of endangered species, and as more go, so we get nearer to the top. Wilford said of the dinosaurs that they were limited; they were incapable of foreseeing or preventing their own extinction. We are no different! Is any one of us able to use our intelligence for the broader good when selfish motives intervene? Why do we accept what the experts tell us? Why are we optimistic about the future but apathetic about destroying the planet? Have we inherited fatal flaws from our predecessors, the dinosaurs?

CHAPTER THIRTEEN

THE DINOSAUR HERITAGE

*"The gigantic catastrophes that threaten us are not
elemental happenings of a physical or biological kind, but are
psychic events... man is exposed to the elemental forces of
his own psyche."*

C.G.Jung

"It is possible for societies to live and prosper with advanced technology."
Sagan calls this the Existence Theorem. The evidence presented here does not
favor it. We have surmised that intelligent dinosaurs, the anthroposaurs,
destroyed their world 65 million years ago. And the omens are that we too are
heading for extinction. At the end of the Cretaceous the vertebrate biomass
concentrated into a few highly populous species. Today the same thing is
happening. Now, mankind, the new intelligent lifeform, breeds the few species
at the expense of the many. Then, it was the intelligent dinosaur. Genetic
variation was narrowed by breeding and environmental destruction until it
virtually did not exist. It was literally genocide – without the genes to cope
with the slightest stresses, the remaining species died off too. History is
repeating itself. The Existence Theorem is bunk!

Why do things tend to repeat themselves? Karl Popper speaks of the
"propensity" that some event will occur. Propensity is probability with intent –
it exerts an influence on events as if it were a physical field like an electric or
gravitational field. It is reminiscent of Sheldrake's morphogenetic fields.
Controversial though they are, these hypotheses imply that when something
occurs, it has more chance of happening again. If true, and the anthroposaurs
have already destroyed themselves, we might be locked into an outcome that
will be nigh on impossible – might *be* impossible – to alter.

Is it our destiny to verify the Existence Theorem or our fate to falsify it.
To verify it we have to break free of a morphogenetic field, to establish a new
propensity. We seem to have less chance of doing so than deflecting an
incoming planetoid. Where is the will to change our behavior? Where is the
mechanism to do it? Do we suffer from the same affliction as the
anthroposaurs and perhaps all intelligent life forms – some self-destructive
syndrome that is a sine qua non of intelligence? If the answer is "yes" we are
doomed. Even if we can see the fault in ourselves, we are powerless to change
it. I believe we have a legacy from the dinosaurs. It is part of our psyche. We
cannot reject it. It is our dinosaur heritage!

What is this syndrome? Strictly we can never know because the
psychology of anthroposaurs is not open to study – we cannot make the
necessary comparisons between ourselves and them. What we can do is study
human psychology and attempt to piece together the elements of the syndrome
in ourselves. To see why warnings of doom have had no effect – why people

do not want to know. There have been many prophets of the forthcoming catastrophe but they are not hailed and praised for their forethought – they are ignored or condemned as Jeremiahs. The human race persists in its willingness to destroy itself and most other higher organisms for selfish economic and ideological reasons, all of them short term.

There is something strange about the way we perceive things. Small disasters in terms of numbers of dead that occur suddenly, unexpectedly, visibly, shock us. But huge disasters dispersed in space and time, we hardly notice. Norman Myers points out that the crash of a jumbo jet attracts media headlines, but no headlines shout out the death of a jumbo jet full of children every 20 minutes, the rate of child mortality in the Third World. Yet the cost of a can of beer every three months to the citizens of the First World would stop this carnage by providing money to implement immunization programs and to prevent diarrhoea in infants. And besides the millions who die every year of disease, starvation and suicide, in the last 200 years perhaps 100 million people have died in warfare. Yet we are totally indifferent to it. We are indifferent to the deaths of our own species as well as to others. Why?

Why are we so perverse? Why are we apathetic about our destruction of the environment and the threats to life we are creating? Why do we allow rapacious industrialists whether of the blue or the red variety to contaminate the earth? Why do we accept the rule of governments that allow them to do it and, through accumulating dangerous armaments and adopting threatening postures, endanger the world in their own way? Why do we retain such an obtuse optimism that we revile those who *do* warn us of the dangers. Why is it so much more virile to accept the status quo rather than criticize it? Why do we do what we are told even when we know it is wrong? Why don't we recognize our dinosaur heritage?

The late Niko Tinbergen, the world famous ethologist, thought there were human characteristics that once were valuable to survival but which, through the speed of the evolution of advanced society, have become so ill-fitted to the needs of technological man that they now threaten us. This idea is compelling because the key characteristic of modern man, as it would have been for anthoposaurus, is the remarkable speed at which technological society emerged, creating conditions quite different from those in which instincts evolved.

It happens elsewhere in nature. Migratory birds like swallows that have a late brood are likely to abandon them to die at the end of the summer if the migratory instinct switches on before the young are mature enough. At one time (perhaps when weather was warmer), they could comfortably raise two broods but now they cannot, and so two instincts conflict. There is a maladaptation. Darwin in "The Descent of Man" thought this was evidence that such animals could feel no remorse, had no conscience, indeed no memory of their action. They seem just to forget the brood when the greater urge presents itself. If so, the swallows did not even recognize what they had done. Are we similar?

So instincts sometimes conflict. When intelligence evolves these conflicts become conscious posing the creature moral dilemmas. It resolves them by inventing rules, laws and morals. With the growth of society the rules themselves condition our behavior. So far so good. But the original code of ethics, made in primitive societies, might not be forever correct. If we have built on behavior maladapted for modern conditions, we shall find that our mores, rules, norms and habits – our very ways of thinking – are leading us to disaster instead of giving us guidelines for a better existence.

"Are the now redundant side-effects of our own evolutionary history not only inappropriate but actually lethal?" asks Norman F.Dixon, a professor of psychology at the University of London. He asks us to consider the following equation:

$$Man + Technology = Extinction.$$

Mankind exists and has invented technology. The combination inevitably leads to mankind's extinction. Can it be avoided? Yes, if we get rid of technology. But technology cannot be disinvented, so extinction can only be prevented by changing the nature of man. Mankind will have to change to prove the Existence Theorem or technology will falsify it. Erich Fromm, the social philosopher, concurs. He writes, "the Falangist motto, 'Long live death', threatens to become the secret principle of a society in which the conquest of nature by the machine constitutes the very meaning of progress, and where the living person becomes an appendix to the machine." In our mechanized, urban societies we have lost the knowledge of our relationships with the rest of the biosphere. Instead we are obsessed with mechanical devices, our cars, TVs, computers and washing machines, and mechanical analysis of the interrelationships between ourselves, our hierarchies, social symbols and selfishness. Not only are we unaware of the stench of death around us, in some unconscious way we revel in it.

Selfish interest might be one characteristic that was valuable in some evolutionary contexts but is no longer. Other motives which developed in evolution to balance against excessive self regard perhaps fail to operate adequately in our coddled environment. "The thing to be lamented is, not that men have so great regard to their own good or interest in the present world, or they have not enough; but that they have so little to the good of others," as Bishop Butler put it – selfishness is not excessive self-love, but indifference to others. Obsessive selfishness seems to overwhelm all other feelings – all obsessions do. Ultimately the obsession destroys even the obsessive. Initially selfish, the behavior eventually contradicts self regard by being self destructive! It becomes a death wish. Necrophilia! "Long live death"! And our society depends upon highly specialized people – experts – who have to be obsessive in their field to succeed. Our society selects for obsessiveness. Entrepreneurs, Presidents, Prime Ministers, Generals, Scientists – successful people must be obsessive! They must be necrophiles!

We begin to see that we have a very odd civilization indeed! Through maladaptation we have become necrophiles – and the most necrophilous of all are the experts. Just like the anthroposaurs?

If the dinosaur heritage comprises a catalogue of maladaptations inclining us toward death, analysis of the human psyche is needed to tease out its elements. Here I discuss three possible components; apathy, obedience to authority, and the dominance of the left brain and its link with obsessive optimism. Each in its different way seems to contribute to our inability to see what we are doing or our inability to respond to it.

Frustration occurs when a goal is blocked by a person or a thing. Animals and humans react to frustration in different ways but aggression and apathy are two common reactions. Inherent aggression stemming from a killer instinct might be part of our problem. But the opposite is also a problem. People can *learn* to react aggressively or apathetically. If aggression in the past (perhaps in childhood) has habitually led to a goal being achieved then aggression is likely to be the learned response to frustrating situations. If aggression has not worked in childhood then people may feel "helpless" to do anything about achieving their objective and become apathetic or depressed.

Experimental studies of both humans and animals have shown that "helplessness", the inability to predict or, especially, to control the environment is psychologically highly damaging, yet helplessness can be "learned".

Dogs are put into a cage where they get electric shocks to their feet. The shocks are unavoidable and, though unpleasant, eventually the dog learns to endure them. The dog is now put in a cage with a second, stress-free compartment accessible simply by jumping a barrier. When given electric shocks, it makes no attempt to escape even though it could easily avoid pain. It has learned to be helpless and to do nothing but endure its torture. It has learned to behave apathetically. Dogs given shocks in the double cage from the beginning quickly learn to escape over the barrier, yet many of the apathetic dogs will not learn how to escape even if the experimenter attempts to show them by physically lifting them into the other compartment.

But is it the electric shock that traumatizes the dog? To test this, experiments have been carried out with rats on treadwheels. Two rats were wired to get shocks in their tails but one rat was given a signal first and then by running the treadwheel faster could delay the shock. This rat had some control over its environment but would, through complacency or tiredness, occasionally fail to pedal and would get the shock anyway. When it did, the other rat got a shock as well. Thus both rats got the same number of shocks but one only had any control over when it got one.

Naturally the situation was stressful for the animals and after running the experiment for a long time the degree of stress could be determined by examining the rats for internal lesions and ulcers. The interesting result was that only the rat that had no control was noticeably stressed. The other animal was physically perfectly healthy. Both had received the same number of shocks so helplessness had produced the stress.

Humans have been tested in similar experiments. In one, subjects saw color slides of people who had died violently. They could change the slide by pressing a button, but a another group had no such control and were obliged to look at the slides for as long as the first group were willing to. Both groups were monitored by measuring skin resistance. It was the group with no control of the situation whose anxiety was highest. Another experiment subjected people to the stress of a loud noise. Again the group without control were worst affected. A refinement of the last experiment showed that even when control was not used, the belief that it was available still lessened stress.

The point is that we are in stressful situations every day, whether at work or participating in normal society. At work, for example, we are the slaves of our air conditioned offices and factories. If 70 degrees Celsius is just right for F. most of us there are still large numbers for whom it is too hot or too cold. The same goes for relative humidity, cigarette fumes, solvent fumes, draughts, micro-organisms, etc., all the constituents, in fact, of a "sick" building. You cannot change things unless sufficient people complain, but, because the conditions are designed to suit the majority, the majority are content. You therefore cannot persuade your bosses that you are being adversely affected. You are helpless.

It goes without saying that, rather than be dismissed, you often have to do jobs at work that you do not like. That too can bring on the apathy of helplessness. In the UK, statisticians in the civil service, under pressure from the executive, had to manipulate their data to show the government in the best light. The statistician values objectivity. It must really hurt to cheat with the figures. What do they do? Lose their jobs and their pension? Or shrug their shoulders and learn helplessness?

We have elections in the belief that governments will carry out policies we want, but our favorites lose, or join a coalition with another party whose policies we do not want, or on election they simply adopt different policies from the ones we voted for. Is it surprising that 30 to 50 per cent of the electorate commonly do not vote. Yet in comparison with totalitarian countries we make failure to vote into a virtue – it proves how free we are. The real message is that many people are resigned, like the dogs and rats I have described, to being punished. They have become passive and often despairing, believing that they cannot influence events so there is no point in trying. Similarly we may all know the planet is dying but we feel helpless about it and so have become apathetic about our fate.

At least in democracies, we can change our leaders. But why do we only too often elect ones that make life unpleasant, that subject us deliberately to stress? One reason is our sense of guilt. Most of us are inculcated with a sense of morality from childhood. Bad behavior is punished by angry parents applying age old codes of ethics. Later, if we do things that we shouldn't, we feel guilty because we have an inbuilt parent – our conscience. That seems straightforward. But, oddly, guilty feelings arise if things go too well. Periods of success and well-being are followed by a need for atonement. In political terms this feeling is frequently expressed by the choice of a leader who offers to relieve our guilt by making us take the medicine. The mood of the electorate can unpredictably swing after a period of affluence from tolerably equitable governments to more extreme ones.

At present, human beings, at least in the advanced countries, seem to be obsessed with maintaining their own lives at higher and higher levels of luxury, yet as Fromm says, "Life mainly concerned with its own maintenance is inhuman." In subconscious atonement for the guilt of our selfishness, are we preparing to sacrifice our lives and maintain in death the humanity which we can see we are losing? Do we justify our drive for this luxurious existence by subliminally accepting that we are committing gigasuicide, self-effacingly cleansing the earth of the parasite that we have become?

According to Professor Stanley Milgram, "a fatal flaw which nature has designed into us and which in the long run gives our species only a moderate chance of survival" is obedience. Milgram is the US professor who carried out a series of experiments to test whether there was any psychological validity in the pleas of Nazis like Eichmann that they were only carrying out orders in committing millions to the gas chambers. Milgram wanted to find out if people would unquestioningly carry out orders to do something which otherwise might be thought uncivilized and contrary to moral conscience.

He advertised for people to help him with experiments on memory. The volunteers had to give the subject simple memory tests – if the subject made a mistake the volunteer had to administer an electric shock and then proceed to the next test. The volunteers briefly saw the subject strapped in a chair, and Milgram demonstrated to them the nature of the punishment by giving them mild shocks of 45 volts. He then took them into the next room where they sat in front of a panel with a set of levers marked with voltage levels up to 450 volts. The top levels were marked "danger – extreme shock." In reality the apparent subject was Milgram's accomplice; the volunteers were the true subjects of the experiment. Milgram, whose voice was, of course, the voice of authority, sat behind the volunteers firmly urging them, if they hesitated, to apply the appropriate shock lest they spoil the experiment.

The results were astounding. With no feedback of sound from the victim, the volunteers blithely pushed the voltage up to the maximum. When the accomplice cursed, objected and cried in pain (all simulated), a minority, but only a minority, refused to inflict further punishment. Some others obeyed but showed signs of conflict and distress.

Later experiments by other workers used a puppy dog subjected to genuine electric shocks. Milgram's results were confirmed. A remarkable fact was that all the women tested were willing to push the voltage up to the maximum when instructed by the authority figure. Women's assumed natural characteristics of caring and mothering seem easily overwhelmed by the voice of authority.

Milgram's experiments on obedience might be considered by many of us to have been invaluable revelations about the way we, as human beings, behave. Yet criticisms by his peers, fellow psychological experts, were severe and damaging: "People should not be duped in this way," they said, "It is unethical". But the volunteers, when told the truth, mainly supported Milgram, commenting that he had discovered one of the most important causes of the trouble in the world, that men should avoid harm to their fellow men even at the risk of violating authority, and that the results were valuable if they jarred people out of their complacency. The experiment obviously could not have been done without misleading the participants. Moreover, Milgram's critics have found other psychological studies on human subjects involving deception perfectly acceptable. Of course, these did not dig at the foundation of "civilized" society – obedience – the essence of our hierarchical structures, society's buttress against anarchy!

Milgram's findings show that many, perhaps most, of us could have been Eichmann. But the general public dupes itself. When people are asked how they would react as volunteers in Milgram's experiments, most guess that they would stop at about 150 volts. Only four per cent believe they would go as far as 300 volts and only one per cent to the maximum.

Exhibit 12. Submission to authority: an aspect of the dinosaur heritage?

Milgram varied the circumstances of the experiments. With the accomplice in the same room as the volunteers, fewer people went to the maximum. When the volunteers had to physically push the accomplice's hand on to the electrode, fewer still obeyed. But when the volunteers took on the role of the authority figure instructing someone else to apply the shock, even more of them were willing to go to the maximum.

We think we are much more willing to defy authority than we are: authority therefore has much more power over us than we think!

At Mi Lai in Vietnam, all-American, middle-class young men butchered 500 old men, women, children and babies. Their officers had ordered that, to improve morale, the Viet Cong in Mi Lai had to be engaged at all costs. If Viet Cong guerrillas had been in the village, as the US generals supposed, they were elusive enough not to be there when the US troops arrived. But this inscrutable oriental tactic did not deter the unscrupulous occidental generals. They defined the Vietnamese still in the village as enemy combatants: anyone there, irrespective of age or sex, became Viet Cong by definition. The GIs killed them. Only a handful of the young soldiers refused to obey!

By yielding to authority we can absolve ourselves of guilt. Like Eichmann, we are doing our duty, only obeying orders: it is not our fault! Furthermore those who give the order also absolve themselves from guilt: they do not have to do the dirty work themselves. A chain of command or a technological device (like a B52 bomber) diffuses the responsibility, reducing guilt more.

Aggressive behavior within species evolved because it increases fitness to reproduce, but, in the vast majority of animals, it is ritualized to minimize injuries serious enough to weaken the species. The weaker of two animals vying for food or a mate, at some point signals its surrender and the fight is over. Hostilities cease promptly because the combatants are in immediate contact. In human society, passing the buck to those lower in the hierarchy, and the intervention of technology, allows fighting to be done at a distance. Then there is no compunction and no surrender. Who cares about the fate of those you cannot see? Young Americans dropping vast tonnages of high explosive bombs from B52 bombers six miles high would not have suffered the guilt feelings even of the ground troops killing face-to-face at Mi Lai. The same applies to those who pollute the environment and rape the world. We feel the benefits but see little of the carnage. We are removed from the outcome. We are absolved of guilt!

Worse. When hostility is pent up and repressed, a person or group of people it is socially acceptable to hate may be chosen as scapegoats. Pent up hostility can be released on them through victimization or pogrom. Then diffusion of responsibility through a chain of command or through technology can be disastrous. Better dead than Red. The shooting down of the Korean Airlines flight 007 so incensed US senior officers that they were willing to risk a nuclear war. They attempted to send a fraudulent intelligence report to the Pentagon to justify retaliatory action that could have ended in a holocaust. The world was saved by an courageous junior soldier. He disobeyed! He refused to send the mendacious dispatch. Milgram's work shows that that young officer was one of a rare minority of people. Mankind had a close shave!

The brain has evolved into two distinct halves connected by several bundles of nerve fibres, the largest of which is the corpus callosum. Normally messages that initially reach one side of the brain pass to the other along these nerve bridges so that both halves of the brain work together. This bilateral division of the brain occurred very early on in evolution. Anthroposaurs, though having brains physiologically different in many ways from human beings, would certainly have had two halves to their brains just as we have.

The division possibly arose as a safety device: if the animal damages part of its brain, it can still function using the other half. It might also, like the multiple computers on the spacecraft, Challenger, have provided fail-safe checking, both halves having to agree before a tricky decision was taken. The two halves in human beings have now developed some functions that are quite different from each other, although each half can take over functions from the other half when necessary. People suffering brain damage in one hemisphere can regain many lost abilities as the undamaged side of the brain learns them.

Broadly speaking the left brain manages language, mathematics, logic and detail while the right brain manages imagination, creativity, dreams, spatial conceptions, recognizing patterns and relationships, intuition and seeing the "whole picture". People differ in the degree to which they use the right hemispheres. Those who make more use of the right brain are divergent thinkers, imaginative, spontaneous and intuitive compared with those who stick with the left hemisphere who tend to be more coldly logical, analytical, keen on organization and concerned with detail. In short, the left brain is generally responsible for rational thinking and the right brain for intuitive. Yet not all right brain inspirations are significant. To determine which ones are, they have to be scrutinized rationally by the left hemisphere. Effective discovery requires both.

Jaynes believes that the dominance of the left brain had its origins only about 3000 years ago. Until then social rules of behavior had emerged from the right brain which processed a welter of experience and returned its findings as dreams or hallucinations, thought to be sent by the gods. Formalized social organizations, writing and the development of culture, and eventually technology put paid to all that and substituted left brain directives and regulations formulated by priests and politicians. "Irrational reasonableness gave way to rational unreasonableness," as Dixon puts it.

In the modern world the left hemisphere's rationality increasingly suppresses the intuitive side. Witness the difficulty of changing a scientific paradigm, the hostility of orthodox thinkers to original thinkers. Yet intuition is more likely to give advanced warning of impending problems. Reason cannot accept that anything is wrong until the full chain of logic is evident. Try to question experts or warn politicians – express sensitivity to matters such as the environment, the plight of the deprived or the dangers of mass destruction, express right brain values – and out come the establishment assassins.

Since the left brain concentrates on detail rather than seeing the whole, one manifestation of it is ignoring the welfare of the mass in favor of the welfare of self, even when self is part of the mass and inevitably must suffer with it – the obsessive selfishness noted earlier. Thus the purveyors of pollution ignore its effects on themselves and their own children. Industrialists in time past happily sought absolution at church while the infants they employed were crippling their bodies and lungs pulling coal trucks deep underground, or working looms in cold satanic mills. The poor immigrants to the USA described in Upton Sinclair's "The Jungle" were literally rotting in chemicals in the meat processing factories in Chicago while the nouveau rich Mr Tycoon sheltered Tycoon Jr and Tycoon III in gracious living. They saw only themselves: left brain logic told them to ignore the wider picture that the right brain attempted to thrust on to them. "That has all changed now," you may protest, but it has not – it is worse. Now most Westerners are Mr Tycoon! We want to preserve our material possessions and demand ever higher standards of living even though continuous economic growth must inevitably destroy the planet. We all lose not just those who are obviously exploited. John Donne's bell is not tolling only for the unfortunates starving in The Sahel – it is tolling for thee, mankind!

Today's industrialist or politician cannot be squeamish about a little atmospheric pollution, a few dead animals or the destruction of more primitive but more sensitive cultures than our own. Their left hemispheres tell them we need more efficiency, higher productivity, greater economic growth and less interference in their right to manage. So much is logical; all else is soft, wimpish and mawkish if not downright Bolshevik. The irony is that it is the left hemisphere that is truly illogical: it will lead to our deaths. It can, with intensity and interest, analyze in academic detail the tiger's fur, tail, muscles, camouflage, claws and teeth. It can debate endlessly about their functions and which are more important than others. But it cannot see the whole animal licking its lips! Only the right brain sees the whole tiger and the danger it poses!

According to Fromm, "we need to create the conditions for mobilizing the love of life, which is the only force that can defeat the love of the dead." Death – extinction – stares us in the face. We can expect no sensible response until that is accepted. Yet, in wars, as Dixon points out, "maundering and baseless optimism are the order of the day" until the foe is actually engaged. Men remain ludicrously optimistic about the outcome of prospective battles until the first blows jolt them, like sleepy drunks, into reality and a hasty and often inadequate defence. Better adapted animals would assess the real situation to be prepared with an appropriate response.

Optimism preserves our peace of mind by evoking positive expectations of future events and a false and deceiving euphoria about possible outcomes. It smacks either of overweening arrogance or of a fear of the outcome that has to be mentally shielded from us – we think that the future will be that which is most preferable to us. Delegates to the Vienna conference on the Chernobyl accident arrived in a thoroughly gloomy and depressed state of mind. Complacency had been shaken. Pessimism! Five days later – Lo! – the gloom had lightened. Optimism! The world's nuclear experts, had convinced themselves there was nothing to worry about. Instead of realistically assessing the implications of Chernobyl, they had thought of lots of reasons why disasters like this were rare except in Russia. They left cheerful and elated. Typically expert: but we all do it – we are all doing it!

What is the source of our baseless optimism? None other than the left brain. The two halves of the brain can be selectively disabled by drugs leaving only the other half functioning. An unchaperoned left brain, the right brain having been drugged, leaves us excessively euphoric: the left brain takes the optimistic, cavalier view by focussing on something familiar, something we can add up or write down, something we "understand". An unchaperoned right brain, the left having been drugged, on the other hand tends to leave us anxious and pensive: it sees the whole situation, its complexity, the hazards, not just the petty details that take our fancy – it scares us, we feel uneasy. The right brain is the entropic brain. It sees the whole results of our actions not just the immediate results. That is what makes it more sensitive and caring.

Carl Sagan tells us that human societies are hierarchical and ritualistic. Suggestions for social change are treated with suspicion. Is there an explanation for this? Paul Maclean, the head of the Laboratory of Brain Evolution and Behavior at the US National Institute of Mental Health, called the center of the forebrain the R-complex where the "R" stands for reptilian because we share it with vertebrates above the reptiles but not with amphibians or fish. He believes it is the source of aggression, territoriality, social hierarchy and ritual. Such irrational properties as emotion have their source in the surrounding layer of forebrain, the limbic system, while rational behavior stems from the large outer shell of the brain, the neocortex. In reptiles, the limbic system is not fully developed and there is no neocortex.

Sagan argues that it is useful to consider the ritualistic and hierarchical aspects of our lives to be strongly influenced by the R-complex and shared with our reptilian forebears; the altruistic, emotional and religious aspects of our lives to be localized to a significant extent in the limbic system and shared with our non-primate mammalian forebears (and perhaps birds); and reason to be a function of the neocortex, shared to some extent with the higher primates and such cetaceans as the dolphins and whales.

Perhaps what we have missed is that the R-complex, though primitive, still exerts a strong influence on the way we behave, conditioning us to perform rituals without any apparent rationality, like people subject to compulsive and obsessive behavior.

There is a worse possibility!

Has the R-complex somehow taken control of the left brain like some mad hacker's computer virus? As the left brain achieved its present dominance has its control by the R-complex become more complete? And has the right brain all the while been trying to warn us against the monster taking over. The right brain is mute and can only give images, mystical impressions and dreams. Nightmares about monsters coming to get us could be the right brain's way of saying that there is a real monster taking over – inside our heads! Apparitions, hauntings, UFO contacts and the menagerie of paranormal creatures that loom out of the night, might be right brain warnings of a threat from something intangible... because it is within.

These manifestations might also be signs that the sleeping anthroposaurs are beginning to rouse!

CHAPTER FOURTEEN

WHO LIES SLEEPING?

"Peace is in the grave.
The grave hides all things beautiful and good:
I am a God and cannot find it there."

P.B.Shelley

That, except for a few final thoughts, is the end of the story.

Why are we perpetually interested in the dinosaurs? There seems an obvious connection with some mythical beasts, most particularly dragons. John Noble Wilford in "The Riddle of the Dinosaurs" draws attention to the battles of mythological heroes like St George, Siegfried and Beowulf with their respective monsters and likens these images to a "struggle with mysterious forces". He argues that such thoughts must be elemental, deeply embedded in the psyche, because they are especially strong in children – whose primeval thought patterns are still unspoiled by experience and tuition. There is even a link with that other legend with which we are fascinated – the vampire – the monster that lies dead by day but comes by night to suck our blood. The root of the word Dracula is the Latin for dragon!

Do we have some mysterious memory of the monstrous beasts? Some psychologists are bold enough to attribute the similarities between the dragons and the dinosaurs to racial memory. The mammals had faced up to the dangers of the dinosaurs for so long and the experience was so terrifying that natural selection saw to it that those creatures which developed an intrinsic image and fear of the dinosaur were more fitted for survival.

Sociobiologists tell us that fundamental behavior patterns, instincts, if you like, are coded in the genes. Then why not racial memories? Plainly there was sufficient time and evolutionary pressure in the 140 million years that the dinosaurs dominated the mammals. Nonetheless, most experts think not. Even if memories could be coded in the genes, they argue that, in the 65 million years since the dinosaurs ceased to be a threat to the mammals, any previous advantage would have disappeared. But is that necessarily true? The point surely about racial memories is that it takes countless years for them to become instilled because such effects are much more subtle and indirect than selection for physical traits. By the same token, they might not be easy to erase. The caution that such a primordial fear instilled in a creature might have given it a lasting advantage – a fear and suspicion that was of benefit even in the world of mammals – the lingering remnants of which we still possess deep in our subconscious minds.

Lyall Watson is one noted biologist who accepts that part of our brain gives us an archaic memory of the dinosaurs. Remember that our brains consist of three parts that developed at different times. The advanced part is the neocortex controlling active thinking, then there is the limbic system which controls emotions, and finally the oldest part is the reptilian complex.

The latter is little more than a pronounced nodule at the top of the spine which has survived essentially unchanged since before the age of the reptiles. This very primitive area of the brain, Watson believes, is the source of primeval, subconscious ideas. Images of dragons are still recorded here and give rise to myths and legends in which the dragon represents inhuman power which has to be tamed or vanquished.

The curious fact about dragon myths is that they seem to anticipate the idea of intelligence in a non-human species. Could these be echoes of the world of the dinosaurs and specifically the civilization of the anthroposaurs? Do they indeed hint at a racial memory of these earlier times?

Just to put these points in context consider briefly some of the myths to which I refer. In Greek mythology, Gaia, the mother of the Gods by Uranus also produced serpents and dragons by Tartarus, the god of the Underworld. The immediate offspring were Typhon and his sister Echidna who incestuously mated to produce Cerberus, the hydra, the serpent, Ladon and the chimaera, amongst others. Echidna had a serpent's body; Typhon had a hundred serpents' heads; cerberus was a three headed dog but had a snake's tale and a row of serpents' heads along his back; the Chimaera had a snake's tale; Hydra was a water serpent. The snake-like features of all these creatures must reflect the reptilian aspects of the dinosaurs.

tail

In Mesopotamia, the role of Gaia was played by Tiamat. Her first brood were gods but they became rather delinquent and their father determined to get rid of them. Tiamat favored the children until they, hearing of their father's displeasure, pre-empted his actions by killing him. This upset mother Tiamat who had a second brood of dragons and serpents to punish her former favorites. The strongest and cleverest of the gods, Marduk, slew the dragons (and his mother for good measure) thus making the world safe for him to create his servant man. Here there is a clear implication that a race of dragons and serpents had to be destroyed before the earth was safe for mankind.

In Norse mythology three monsters fathered by Loki, a sort of fallen angel, are shut away by Thor, but the legend has it that, in time, the three will escape and return to the earth. Cataclysmic earthquakes, volcanoes, poisonous gases, tidal waves and even an ice age are predicted, as a result of which mankind will become extinct until they are restored in a new Garden of Eden and the cycle continues. This myth suggests the frightening prospect that the monsters will re-emerge amidst cataclysm and pollution, destroying mankind and reclaiming the earth. Have we created the conditions for the primordial captives to escape Thor's prison?

The serpent of The Garden of Eden in the Bible, which led to Adam's fall, was not a snake. God punished the creature, for tempting Eve, with the command "crawl on your belly". Previously it must have had limbs to support it, but thenceforth it became a snake. The Bible also described the tempter as the most cunning animal God had made! Curiously, before the Garden of Eden there had been "men" on earth. On the sixth day of creation "God created Human beings, making them like himself" – note the plural. Our ancestor, Adam, the first true man, was only made later in the Biblical creation story.

These are fascinating legends. They all seem to suggest that dragons or serpents, one "the most cunning animals God had made" and evidently sufficiently human in appearance to merit being called "men" in the Bible, lived upon earth before mankind, fell from grace and are possibly waiting their chance to return.

If they are waiting, could they be sending us messages? Are they saying, "We are rousing, humans. You had your chance and failed. It is our turn again"? Are some people particularly receptive to these messages?

H.P.Lovecraft anticipated the idea of intelligent dinosaurs in his story, "The Nameless City", written in 1921. It was the first story recognizably in his Cthulhu series (termed by later admirers, the Cthulhu Mythos). The Nameless City of the title had been built in distant times by a race of intelligent dinosaurs depicted in sculptured low reliefs on the cyclopean stones of the ancient city.

August Derleth in 1945 quoted Lovecraft as having explained: "All my stories, unconnected as they may be, are based on the fundamental lore or legend that this world was inhabited at one time by another race who, in practising black magic, lost their foothold and were expelled, yet live on the outside, ever ready to take possession of the earth again". Advanced technology could be described as magic and its accompanying pollutant effects are undoubtedly black!

Later stories filled out the original idea though not in a consistent way. In "The Call Of Cthulhu" of 1926, the pivotal tale in the group, one of the characters describes Lovecraft's "theory". "There had been aeons when other Things ruled on the earth, and They had had great stone cities. Remains... were still to be found as cyclopean stones... They all died vast epochs of time before man came, but there were arts which could revive Them when the stars had come round again to the right positions in the cycle of eternity... They all lay in Their great city of R'lyeh..."

Further explanation is furnished in "The Dunwich Horror" of 1928: "Nor is it to be thought, that man is either the oldest or the last of earth's masters, or that the common bulk of life and substance walks alone. The Old Ones were, the Old Ones are, and the Old Ones shall be. Not in the spaces we know but between them, they walk serene and primal, undimensioned and by us unseen." One of the weird characters in the story is savaged by guard dogs and is found to have a tail and "legs like a flesh eating dinosaur".

In Lovecraft's stories, the ancient beings communicate with certain human beings by telepathy in dreams or by visions. Meanwhile they are lying waiting; sleeping until the time comes for them to resume their rule.

Although this gamut of ideas was presented as fantasy, is it possible that it is real and, indeed, that Lovecraft was one of the people receiving dream messages from these sleeping creatures? Lovecraft was certainly odd in many ways. According to his biographer, L Sprague de Camp, he suffered from the disease poikilothermism – he was cold blooded! Not fully so, of course, but his body temperature was only partially regulated internally. In the hottest weather, when everyone else wilted, Lovecraft was at his best, bouncing with energy. But even at 70 degrees Fahrenheit (20 degrees Celsius) he was beginning to lose his zest and in winter he could hardly move from his room. When he did venture forth he sometimes passed out from the cold. He also had a cold and deathly handshake. Did he have the same degree of warm blood as the dinosaurs?

Many of the ideas for his stories evidently came in dreams, or images that he had when he visited old buildings and places; (he loved anything antiquarian). Yet, if he were getting telepathic visions of some kind he never realized or admitted it himself and always remained entirely rational. He pooh poohed mediums and astrologers.

He was not rational however in his incredible ideas of class and racial superiority in which he felt himself to be of a higher breed. He described the poor and the immigrants of the time as "squat, squint-eyed jabberers with coarse ways and alien emotions" whom his "deepest cell tissue hates and loathes as the mammal hates and loathes the reptile, with an instinct as old as history..." Isn't that a powerful and suggestive simile? The reference to the mammal's hatred and loathing of the reptile reflects the equal or greater hatred and loathing of the mammal by the reptile, uttered thus to make sense in a mammalian world, yet expressing the feeling of the outcast dinosaurs. Could Lovecraft have been voicing the views of the sleeping inheritors? Was he a human so thoroughly influenced by the sleepers that his own physiology was affected.

Not only was his temperature regulation odd, Lovecraft was also totally unenthusiastic about sex. He deserted his attractive wife and yet condemned homosexuality. Apparently he could not stand *any* intimate contact with human beings. Indeed he wrote: "No effort would have seemed worth my exerting, if it could not earn me a place among those of my own mental type, free from common alien social contacts and influences" – the "alien social contacts and influences" seemed to mean all those of the human race.

Interestingly, another theme of Lovecraft's was that of degeneration. He often wrote about human beings degenerating to rat-like creatures, living in warrens, sewers and burrows. Mutatis mutandis, this conjures up images of the last days of the anthroposaurs, as they degenerated to contorted ciphers of their former selves. What lifeform would most vividly depict degeneration to an intelligent dinosaur? That of the loathsome rat-like mammals that scurried about the anthroposaurs' polluted cities, living in burrows and sewers, thriving on the waste and decay, while the "superior" creatures fought a losing battle to maintain a spaceship earth.

Perhaps I am getting too speculative. Let me come to a conclusion. Are we willing to yield up the earth, whether to the dragon or to the worm? Will we succeed in throwing off the shadow of the serpent and disown the dinosaur heritage? Or are we caught in one of Rupert Sheldrake's morphogenetic fields and are destined to self destruct as surely as common salt has always crystallized as cubes and not hexagons?

Are we locked into ritual ways of behaving – helpless resignation, mechanical left brain thinking, purblind optimism and obedience to the authority of dictatorial experts and governments? The only way we can find out is to make an effort: we have to reject behaviors and rituals that are plainly leading us and the world to destruction. Time is running out.

The earth, like mother Tiamat, can replace us with monsters. The obligatory principle of our lives should be not to offend the earth whether directly or indirectly. All other laws follow from this one.

Two hundred years ago Cuvier warned his generation: "the present era will be reproached if we do not conserve for the future..." Two hundred years on little seems to have been learned and the situation is infinitely worse. No doubt there is comfort in knowing that there will be nobody left to reproach us, or even to gloat over our stupidity. Unless when we have gone... the sleepers awake!

BIBLIOGRAPHY

Since this work is not a book for scholars, I have not given detailed textual references, nor have I compiled an extensive bibliography. The books listed here are the principle source books used. Most of them *do* give extensive references and anyone wishing to study any of the topics covered herein can do worse than to start with this list of books.

Allaby, Michael, "Ecology Facts," London, Hamlyn, 1986
Allaby, Michael and Lovelock, James E., "The Great Extinction," London, Secker and Warberg, 1983
Attenborough, David, "Life on Earth", London, Collins/BBC, 1979
Bakker, Robert, "The Dinosaur Heresies," London, Penguin, 1988
Bellini, James, "High Tech Holocaust," Newton Abbot, David and Charles, 1986
Calder, Nigel, "Timescale", London, Chatto and Windus, 1984
Charig, Alan, "A New Look at the Dinosaurs", London, Heineman, 1979
Dawkins, Richard, "The Blind Watchmaker", Harlow, Longman, 1986
De Camp, L Sprague, "Lovecraft, A Biography", London, New English Library, 1976
Denton, M., "Evolution; A Theory in Crisis", London, Burnett, 1985
Desmond, Adrian J., "The-Hot Blooded Dinosaurs", London, Futura, 1977
Dixon, Norman F., "Our Own Worst Enemy," London, Jonathan Cape, 1987
Gribbon, John and Cherfas, Jeremy, "The Monkey Puzzle," London, Triad/Paladin, 1983
Gould, Stephen Jay, "The Flamingo's Smile", London, Pelican, 1986
Hoyle, Fred, "Ice", London, Hutchinson, 1981
Johanson, Donald C. and Edey, Maitland A., "Lucy, the Beginnings of Humankind", Granada, London, 1981
Leakey, Richard E., "The Making of Mankind", London, Abacus, 1982
Leith, Brian, "The Descent of Darwin", London, Collins, 1982
Lovelock, James E., "Gaia: a New Look at Life on Earth," Oxford, OUP, 1979
Midgley, Mary, "Wickedness", London, Routledge and Kegan Paul, 1984
Morgan, Elaine, "The Aquatic Ape", London, Souvenir Press, 1982
Myers, Norman, "The Sinking Ark," London, Pergamon, 1979
Nicholls, Peter (Editor), "The Science in Science Fiction", London, Michael Joseph, 1982
Norman, David, "The Illustrated Encyclopaedia of Dinosaurs", London, Salamander, 1985
Sagan, Carl, "The Dragons of Eden," London, Hodder and Stoughton, 1977
Steiger, Brad, "Worlds Before Our Own", New York, Berkley, 1979
Watson, Lyall, "Earthworks", London, Hodder and Stoughton, 1986
Wilford, John Noble, "The Riddle of the Dinosaurs", London, Faber and Faber, 1986

About the author

Mike Magee was born in Leeds, Yorkshire, in 1941.

He attended Cockburn High School in South Leeds then studied for a degree at the Royal Military College of Science. After graduating from the University of London, he obtained a higher degree at the University of Aston and a teaching qualification at Huddersfield.

He carried out research at the Universities of Aston and Bradford, and at the Wool Industries Research Association then taught for seven years in Devon. He moved to London and for ten years was an advisor for the UK government.

He has written over a dozen scientific papers and about forty publications for the government.

Now retired in Somerset he attempts to dull his fervid imagination with the local cider and, though he quite often succeeds, he does not blame it for this book.

He has three adult children.